HIGH NOON

IDENTIFYING THE SEQUENCE • IDENTIFYING DETAILS

READING

UNDERSTANDING THE MAIN IDEA • USING CONTEXT

COMPREHENSION

DRAWING CONCLUSIONS • MAKING INFERENCES

LEVEL C

Deborah Akers

HIGH NOON BOOKS

Available from High Noon Books

High Noon Reading Comprehension Program

Level A	ISBN 1-57128-186-X
Level B	ISBN 1-57128-187-8
Level C	ISBN 1-57128-188-6
Level D	ISBN 1-57128-189-4

Cover Design by Lucy Neilson

High Noon Books
A division of Academic Therapy Publications
20 Commercial Boulevard
Novato, CA 94949-6191
800-422-7249

International Standard Book Number 1-57128-188-6
ISBN 13: 978-1-57128-188-3

20 19 18 17 16 15 14 13 12 11
15 14 13 12 11 10 09 08 07 06

TABLE OF CONTENTS

TO THE TEACHER

High Noon Reading Comprehension is designed to give your students strategies and opportunities for practice that will improve their reading comprehension skills.

Program Features

Each unit contains a series of six lessons that provide the following elements:

- Grade 3 reading level
- Unit opener comprehension strategies lesson
- Vocabulary lessons
- Reading passages that gradually increase in length
- A range of high-interest topics from a variety of genres and subject areas
- Review lessons at the end of each unit

How to Use These Lessons

Provide students with a copy of the Answer Sheet found on page 78 of this book. As students become familiar with the format of the book, lessons may be completed independently. However, specific direct explanations of strategies, modeling, guided practice, and feedback will support your students' efforts and can contribute significantly to their success.

Strategy Lessons. For the first lesson of each unit, read together the unit opener strategy lesson. Discussing the strategies and answering students' questions at this stage will help them prepare to read strategically.

Vocabulary Words. Specific discussion of the words listed in each lesson may be beneficial.

1. Write the vocabulary words on the board.
2. Assist students with any difficult pronunciations.
3. Read together the example sentences and discuss the meaning of each word.
4. Ask students to use each word in a sentence. Write that sentence on the board.

Modeling Reading. You can demonstrate how to use a strategy by modeling the process of strategic reading. Read aloud the first few lines of a passage, asking questions as you read to reinforce comprehension.

Guided Practice. Ask students to read the first paragraph or the first few sentences of the selection. Discuss what they have read in light of the lesson's strategy focus.

Feedback. When the students have completed a lesson, answers can be checked with the Answer Key on pages 79-80. The number correct can be entered on the Progress Chart found on the Answer Sheet. Take the opportunity to review items missed at this point and return to the lesson for further instruction if necessary.

TO THE STUDENT

Reading is a very important skill. It helps you learn about many new things. You can learn about almost anything by reading about it. You can learn more about sports and animals. You can learn about how to make things. You can enjoy a good adventure story. Reading opens up the world.

Good readers use tricks, or "strategies," to help them understand what they read. The strategies you will learn in this book are—

- Identifying the Sequence
- Identifying Details
- Using the Context
- Understanding the Main Idea
- Drawing Conclusions
- Using Inference

How to Use This Book

- Your teacher will help you decide which skills you need to practice. For each unit go to the first lesson. Read the strategies. Then read the vocabulary words. Ask questions if there are words you do not understand.

- Follow the directions and read the passages. Remember to think about what you are reading.

- Answer the questions after each passage. Mark your answers on the Answer Sheet.

- When you are done with the lesson, check your answers with the Answer Key.

- Record how many answers you got right on the Progress Chart.

This book is meant to help you become a better reader. Think about the strategies you learn. Also enjoy the stories. Don't worry if you miss some of the questions. The important thing is to do your best. Reading takes practice, just like sports. The more you practice, the better you'll get and the more you'll enjoy reading!

UNIT 1
LESSON 1

VOCABULARY

salary . . . . . money you make working

hammock . . a swinging bed that hangs

terminal . . . a place where people get off boats or planes

recipe . . . . . . a list that tells how to make something

ferry . . . . a boat that carries people

mayonnaise . . a sandwich spread

Read each passage. Then choose the correct answer for each question.

THE DOG WALKER

Skip needed to make some money. Scoop said Skip could walk his dog every day. He would get a salary of five dollars. Skip took the dog to the park. On his way, he passed Jan. She asked Skip to walk her dog, too. Soon, Skip was walking five dogs! It was a fun job.

1 What happened first?

    A. Skip got five dollars.
    B. Skip needed some money.
    C. Skip walked Scoop's dog.
    D. Skip passed Jan.

2 What happened last?

    A Skip walked Scoop's dog.
    B. Skip saw Jan.
    C. Skip walked five dogs.
    D. Skip passed Jan.

THE LOST BOOK

Meg could not find her book. She looked all over the house. Then she looked out in the yard. Kate was sitting reading in the hammock. "I lost my book," said Meg. "You should try this book," said Kate. " I found it in my car." "That's where I left it!" cried Meg. Kate had her book!

3 What happened first?

A. Kate had her book.
B. Meg couldn't find her book.
C. Kate was sitting outside.
D. Meg went out in the yard.

4 What happened last?

A. Kate was in the yard.
B. Meg could not find her book.
C. Meg looked in the house.
D. Kate had Meg's book.

MAKING BUTTER

It is easy to make your own butter. First, you get some milk or cream. Pour it in a big jar. Close the lid tightly. Then shake the jar for awhile. Soon, the milk will get lumpy. Those lumps are butter. Spread them on some toast.

5 What should you do first?

A Close the jar.
B. Get some milk.
C. Shake the jar.
D. Have some butter.

6 What should you do next?

A Put the milk in a jar.
B. Close the jar tightly.
C. Shake the jar awhile.
D. Spread it on some toast.

THE TRIP

Meg wanted to visit her grandma. Her grandma lives on an island. Meg drove her car onto a ferry. Meg went up to the deck. Soon she could see the island's shore. She could see her grandma waiting for her at the terminal. She waved and waved.

7 What did Meg do first?

A. Drove her car onto the ferry.
B. She waved to her grandma.
C Went up to the ferry deck.
D. Saw her grandma on the shore.

8 What did Meg do last?

A. Went up on the deck.
B. Waved at her grandma.
C. Wanted to visit her grandma.
D. Drove her car onto the ferry.

THE BEST TUNA

Here is the best recipe for tuna. You mix in some mayonnaise. Add some mustard if you like. Then put in a little chopped onion and celery. Add a little lemon juice. Add some salt and pepper. Spread it on your favorite bread. Or you can put it in a salad.

9 What should you do first?

A. Chop onion and celery.
B. Mix in some mayonnaise.
C. Add salt and pepper.
D. Spread it on bread.

10 What should you do last?

A. Put it on some bread.
B. Add chopped celery.
C. Add some lemon juice.
D. Mix in some mayonnaise.

Now use the Answer Key to check your answers. Mark the number you got correct on the Progress Chart.

LESSON 2

VOCABULARY

noticed . . . . saw for the first time
fantastic . . . really great
costumes . . . funny clothes

stilts . . . . tall sticks you can walk on
details . . . . . small parts
shrunk . . . . . made smaller

Read each passage. Then choose the correct answer for each question.

THE STRANGE CAR

Scoop Doogan got in his car. He went to pick up Skip. They were going to the car show together. After Skip got in, Scoop noticed there was a car following them. Scoop stopped the car. "I'll talk to that guy," he said. The man came up to their car instead. He said, "Your car is fantastic! I want to show it at the car show!" They all went to the car show together. Scoop's car was a big hit.

1 What happened first?

   A. Scoop noticed another car.
   B. The man came up to the car.
   C. Scoop went to pick up Skip.
   D. Scoop's car was a hit.

2 What happened last?

   A. They all went to the car show.
   B. Scoop noticed a strange car.
   C. Scoop went to talk to the man.
   D. Scoop went to pick up Skip.

CHOPPING WOOD

Meg's family was at the cabin. Meg's dad went to chop wood. Meg decided she wanted to learn how to chop wood. First, her dad picked a good piece of wood. He set it on its end. He took a swing with his ax. It chopped halfway through the wood. Then he hit it again. This time, the wood split in half. Then Meg tried it. Together, they made a great big pile of firewood.

3 What did Meg's dad do first?

   A. He went outside to chop wood.
   B. He took a swing with his ax.
   C. He made a pile of wood.
   D. He split the wood in half.

4 What happened last?

   A. Meg tried to chop some wood.
   B. He picked up a piece of wood.
   C. They went up to their cabin.
   D. They made a big pile of wood.

CHINESE NEW YEAR

It was Chinese New Year. Scoop and Skip went to the parade. There were lots of people on the sidewalks. Everyone was excited for the parade to begin. First there were some kids on horses. They had fancy costumes. Next came a great band. Then there were more people dressed in costumes. They were walking on stilts. Finally, there were fireworks. A huge dragon came down the street. There were people making the dragon go. It was the best part of the parade!

5 What came first in the parade?
   A. A great band.
   B. Kid on horses.
   C. People in costumes.
   D. A huge dragon.

6 What came next in the parade?

   A. A great band.
   B. Fireworks.
   C. People on stilts.
   D. Kids on horses.

7 What came last in the parade?

   A. Kids on horses.
   B. People on stilts.
   C. A great band.
   D. A huge dragon.

STAMPS

Have you ever looked closely at a stamp? Many stamps are more than just something to put on a letter. They are like small works of art. It is not easy to make the art for a stamp. First, the picture must be made large. That is so you can see all the details. It has to be drawn perfectly. Then the picture is shrunk down. If it still looks good, they may choose it to make a stamp.

8 To make a picture for a stamp, what happens first?

   A. The picture is shrunk down.
   B. The stamp goes on a letter.
   C. The picture is drawn large.
   D. They choose it to make a stamp.

9 What happens next?

   A. They find a large picture.
   B. The picture is shrunk down.
   C. They make some new stamps.
   D. They choose it to make a new stamp.

10 What happens last?

   A. The picture is drawn large.
   B. The picture may be chosen for a stamp.
   C. The picture may have to be drawn again.
   D. The picture may have to get smaller.

Now use the Answer Key to check your answers. Mark the number you got correct on the Progress Chart.

LESSON 3

VOCABULARY

pointed . . . . with a sharp top
enemies . . . . people who want to hurt you

chimp . . . . . . a kind of monkey
Africa . . . . . . a large continent

Read each passage. Then choose the correct answer for each question.

TIPIS

Long ago, the Plains Indians were hunters. They didn't live in one place. They followed the animals that they hunted. They had to have houses that they could move quickly. That is where tipis (say tee•peez) came from. The houses looked like pointed tents.

To make a tipi, first you cut long, straight poles. You need about ten of them. Then you set up the poles in a circle on the ground. All the poles lean in. The tops of the poles come together. Finally, you take a big piece of cloth. You put it over the poles. You can camp out in your tipi!

1 To make a tipi, what do you do first?

A. Camp out in your tipi.
B. Cut long, straight poles.
C. Put the poles together.
D. Set the poles in a circle.

2 What do you do next?

A. Cut long, straight poles.
B. Get a big piece of cloth.
C. Camp out in your tipi.
D. Set the poles in a circle.

3 What do you do last?

A. Put cloth over the poles.
B. Put the poles in a circle.
C. Cut about ten poles.
D. Find ten straight poles.

A MONKEY IN SPACE

Before people went up in space, animals did. The first one was a chimp named Ham. He only went up for 16 minutes. The second chimp in space was named Enos. He went around the earth in a spaceship. The trip lasted over three hours!

While Enos was flying, he had work to do. He did several science projects. He could also eat and drink during the trip.

After his trip, Enos landed in the ocean. A boat picked up the spaceship. When they opened the door, Enos hopped out. He took a breath of fresh air. He shook hands with all the people on the boat! Enos was very happy to be back on Earth.

4 What was the last thing to happen to Enos?

    A. He went up in a spaceship.
    B. He traveled for three hours.
    C. He landed in the ocean.
    D. He ate and drank in space.

5 What did Enos do up in space?

    A. He did science projects.
    B. He shook people's hands.
    C. He went up in space.
    D. He jumped in the ocean.

6 What did Enos do after his spaceship landed?

    A. He went swimming.
    B. He took a breath of fresh air.
    C. He did some work up in space.
    D. He went up in space.

THE END OF THE DODO BIRDS

Once there were birds called dodoes. They lived on some islands near Africa. The dodoes had short, stubby wings. They were very fat. The birds could not fly. Dodoes did not have claws. They didn't have sharp beaks. They couldn't fight. But they didn't need to fly or fight. The dodo birds had no enemies.

Then some men came to the island. The men brought monkeys with them. They also brought pigs with them. Soon the men began to take the dodoes' eggs. They ate them. So did the monkeys and the pigs.

The men chased the dodo birds. They killed them for food. So did the monkeys and pigs. Now the dodoes needed wings. They needed to fight, but they couldn't. So, one by one, the dodo birds died. And then they were all gone.

7 What happened first?

    A. The dodoes flew away.
    B. Men came to the island.
    C. The men took dodo eggs.
    D. Dodoes lived on an island.

8 What happened next?

    A. The dodoes went away.
    B. Monkeys chased the dodoes.
    C. Men came to the island.
    D. The dodo birds died.

9 What happened after that?

    A. Monkeys chased the dodoes.
    B. Men left the island.
    C. All the dodo birds died.
    D. Dodoes lived on an island.

10 What happened last?

    A. Dodoes did not have wings.
    B. All the dodo birds died.
    C. Men saved the dodos.
    D. Men came to the island.

Now use the Answer Key to check your answers. Mark the number you got correct on the Progress Chart.

LESSON 4

VOCABULARY

frustrated . . upset
engine . . . . . a machine that make a car or plane run
parachute . . a big cloth umbrella

Alaska . . . . . . the biggest state in the United States
medicine . . . . drugs that help people get better

Read each passage. Then choose the correct answer for each question.

POTATO SOUP

Dave wanted to make potato soup. Dave asked his little brother, Jack, to get potatoes for him. Jack looked in the bag. He pulled out a big potato. Then Jack laughed. The potato looked like someone's head. It had two bumps for eyes and a bump for a nose. "This potato is too funny to use," said Jack.

Jack looked for another potato. He pulled out a small one. It looked like a shoe! "This one is too neat to use," he said.

Next, Jack found a potato that looked like a duck. Then he found one that looked like a boat. Jack kept pulling out potatoes. He made up a story for each one.

Dave was frustrated. "I give up," he said. He made bean soup instead.

1 Which happened last?

A. Dave said, "I give up."
B. Dave wanted to make soup.
C. Jack looked for potatoes.
D. Dave made some bean soup.

2 What happened after Jack pulled out the first potato?

A. Dave made some bean soup.
B. Jack laughed at the potato.
C. Dave wanted to make soup.
D. Dave said "I give up."

3 What happened first?

A. Dave wanted to make potato soup.
B. Dave said, "I give up."
C. Dave made some bean soup.
D. Jack saw funny potatoes.

THE LONG DIVE

One day, a man was flying his small plane. There were storm clouds below him. Suddenly, something went wrong. The plane's engine stopped working. Then it started to fall! The man knew he had to get out of the plane. He put on a parachute. Then he jumped out of the plane!

Down and down he fell. As he fell, he looked at his watch. It said 6:05. Then he opened his parachute. Now he felt safer. But he fell right into the storm clouds! The wind hit him. Then it spun him around, and he was flying UP! The wind threw him all over.

At last, the man landed on the ground. He looked at his watch. It said 6:40! He had been in the air for more than 30 minutes!

4 What happened first?

A. The man jumped with his parachute.
B. The plane's engine stopped working.
C. A man was flying in his plane.
D. The man landed on the ground.

5 What time was it when the man jumped?

A. 8:40
B. 6:05
C. 6:40
D. 8:05

6 What happened last?

A. The man landed on the ground.
B. The man's watch read 6:05.
C. The man fell in a big storm.
D. The man went up in a plane.

A BRAVE DOG

There was a dog named Balto. He lived in Alaska. He saved many people's lives. The people in his town were sick. Doctors did not have the right medicine.

There was a big town that had the medicine. But it was over 800 miles away. It was winter, and people could not get there. The snow was too deep to drive in. The only way to get through was by dog sled. Teams of dogs would drag a sled.

Balto was on the last dog team. His team started out in a bad snowstorm. People were afraid the team would get lost. But Balto and his team did not get lost. They kept going until they got home. People cheered when they saw Balto coming! People took the medicine and got better. Balto saved the day!

7 What happened first?

A. Many people in Balto's town were sick.
B. Balto's team went through a big storm.
C. Balto's team got the medicine home.
D. The dogs dragged the sled.

8 What was happening when Balto's team started out on the trip?

A. People took the medicine.
B. Everyone cheered.
C. It was snowing hard.
D. Many lives were saved.

9 What happened when people saw Balto coming?

A. They took turns dragging the sled.
B. They were very sick.
C. They got on a sled.
D. They all cheered.

10 What happened last?

A. A bad snowstorm started.
B. The medicine saved lives.
C. Balto got lost in the snow.
D. The people were sick.

Now use the Answer Key to check your answers. Mark the number you got correct on the Progress Chart.

LESSON 5

VOCABULARY

command .. an order someone gives   **challenges** .... things that are hard to do

relaxed .... felt better   **determination** .. trying very hard

athlete .... someone who does sports   **encouraged** ... tried to help

Read each passage. Then choose the correct answer for each question.

A GOOD DOG

Meg had a new pup named Jimmy. Jimmy was a good dog. Meg loved him a lot. But sometimes he liked to play a little too much. He would chew on Meg's shoes. Jimmy thought everything was a toy! Meg had a problem!

She decided that she would train Jimmy. The first thing she had to do was teach Jimmy to wear a collar. Then she could tug on the collar to tell Jimmy what to do. Jimmy didn't like the collar at first. But Meg patted his head and gave him some treats. Finally he relaxed.

The next thing Meg had to teach was some simple commands. First, she taught him to "Stand." She did that by gently tugging on his collar.

Next, she taught him to "Sit." She did that by gently pushing on his back legs. Soon he was in a sitting position.

Finally, Meg taught Jimmy the "Down" command. This was the hardest one. She took his front legs and slid them down in front of him. That was a little hard for Jimmy to understand. But he finally got it.

Meg was proud. She gave Jimmy a reward. They played ball all afternoon.

1　What was the first thing Meg taught Jimmy?

   A. How to catch a ball.
   B. The "Stand" command.
   C. How to wear a collar.
   D. The "Sit" command.

2　What was the next thing Meg did?

   A. Threw the ball for Jimmy.
   B. Taught the "Stand" command.
   C. Taught the "Sit" command.
   D. Got a new dog.

3　What was the last command Meg taught?

   A. "Sit"
   B. "Stand"
   C. "Down"
   D. "Up"

4 Which was the hardest command?

    A. "Up"
    B. "Sit"
    C. "Stand"
    D. "Down"

5 What was the last thing Meg and Jimmy did?

    A. Played ball together.
    B. Practiced a command.
    C. Played with the cat.
    D. Got a new dog.

A SPECIAL ATHLETE

Carla Shipp was at the helm of the boat. The water was choppy. Carla had to work fast to keep the boat afloat. Soon the boat crossed the finish line. They had won the race! Carla got her first gold medal in the Special Olympics.

Carla has also won other challenges in her life. Her first challenge was when she was little. Carla could not speak until she was nine years old. It took her years to learn to say simple things. But she did like to run and swim. Her mother signed her up for the Special Olympics. Carla ran races and swam. At first, she did not win. But she tried really hard, and it helped her feel good about herself.

When Carla learned to sail, she found things to help her. She made the ropes on the right red and the ropes on the left yellow. That helped her remember right and left. Carla did not let anything stop her from learning. Her determination helped her win a gold medal.

After the race, Carla spoke to a big group of people. She told her story. She also encouraged other athletes to keep trying. It took a lot of courage for Carla to speak. The crowd stood up and clapped and clapped for her.

6 What was Carla's first challenge?

    A. She ran a race when she was nine.
    B. She could not speak until she was nine.
    C. She did not know how to sail a boat.
    D. She did not win the race.

7 What did Carla do her first time in the Special Olympics?

    A. She told her story.
    B. She won a gold medal.
    C. She sailed a boat.
    D. She ran races and swam.

8 What did Carla do to win a gold medal?

    A. She spoke to a group.
    B. She sailed on a boat.
    C. She ran races and swam.
    D. She could not speak.

9 What did Carla do after the boat race?

    A. She spoke to a group of people.
    B. She stopped sailing.
    C. She could not speak to people.
    D. She went to the Special Olympics.

10 What happened last?

    A. The crowd wanted to go sailing.
    B. Carla wanted to sail better.
    C. The crowd clapped and clapped.
    D. Carla could not speak.

Now use the Answer Key to check your answers. Mark the number you got correct on the Progress Chart.

LESSON 6

VOCABULARY

roller coaster . . a ride that goes up and down

REM (rapid eye movement) . . when the eyes are moving around during sleep

researchers . . . people who study things

experiments . . tests that prove something

Read the passage. It is an article about sleep. It tells about different ways that we sleep. Then choose the correct answer for each question.

HOW DO YOU SLEEP?

Sleep is a simple thing, right? You get tired, and then you drift off to sleep. After about eight hours, you wake up again. There is a little more to it than that. The body rides a kind of "roller-coaster" during the night. Surprised? Let's look at it more closely.

Researchers say that sleep has four stages. Stage 1 starts when we just fall asleep. Then we are in between waking and sleeping. The muscles start to relax. Stage 2 goes even deeper. Our muscles relax even more.

Stages 3 and 4 are called deep sleep. We may move around during these stages. But we are very relaxed. It is also when the body takes care of itself. Experiments show that the body builds new cells during sleep.

After Stage 4, something funny happens. It is called REM (rapid eye movement) sleep. In REM sleep, the brain wakes up a little. The eyes are closed, but

they move. They go back and forth, like when you are watching something. This is the time when you are dreaming. Your mind is seeing pictures. But your body is still asleep. The muscles are very still.

A normal night's sleep goes like this. You start out with Stage 1, then go to Stage 2. Then you go to Stages 3 and 4. Then comes a time of REM sleep. That is where the roller coaster comes in. Your body goes down to Stage 4 sleep, and then it goes up to REM sleep. This happens about four times a night. Sounds tiring? It is really the best way to sleep.

Lack of deep sleep can be a very big problem. If you do not get the sleep you need, you can forget things. You could also get sick more often. We all need times of deep sleep.

REM sleep helps the brain stay healthy. Most researchers say REM sleep helps us learn better. There is a saying: "You snooze, you lose." It is really the other way around. It you <u>don't</u> snooze, you lose!

1 What happens in Stage 1 sleep?

   A. You wake up relaxed.
   B. You are in between waking and
      sleeping.
   C. You have lots of interesting dreams.
   D. You cannot get to sleep.

2 What happens in Stages 3 and 4?

   A. You are in between waking and
      sleeping.
   B. You have lots of interesting dreams.
   C. Your muscles get very relaxed.
   D. You cannot get back to sleep.

3 What happens during REM sleep?

   A. You have lots of dreams.
   B. You cannot get to sleep.
   C. You move around a lot.
   D. You are almost awake.

4 When does REM sleep usually happen?

   A. During Stage 1.
   B. Before Stage 2.
   C. After Stage 2.
   D. After Stage 4.

5 When do your eyes go back and forth?

   A. In Stage 2 sleep.
   B. In Stage 3 sleep.
   C. In REM sleep.
   D. In Stage 1 sleep.

6 How many times do we have REM
   sleep?

   A. About ten times a night.
   B. About four times a night.
   C. Only once in a night.
   D. Once a week.

7 How many times do we usually have
   Stage 4 sleep?

   A. Only once in a night.
   B. About 20 times a night.
   C. About four times a night.
   D. About three times a day.

8 When does the body build new cells?

   A. REM sleep.
   B. Stage 1.
   C. Stage 2.
   D. Stages 3 and 4.

9 What could happen if you do not get
   deep sleep?

   A. You might get sick.
   B. You might have dreams.
   C. You might not be relaxed.
   D. You might wake up.

10 What happens after you get REM
    sleep?

    A. You can remember your dreams.
    B. You can learn things better.
    C. You relax your muscles.
    D. You can ride a roller coaster.

Now use the Answer Key to check your answers. Mark the number you got correct on the Progress Chart.

UNIT 2
LESSON 7

Skill Focus: Identifying Details

Certain parts of the story are more important that other parts. Identifying facts will help you understand what you read.

Here are some clues to help you:

- Read carefully.
- Look for the small parts of a story that are important.
- Find the meanings for words you do not know.
- Reread the selection to make sure you have found the important details.

VOCABULARY

enormous ... very big

cruise ...... a ride on a boat

decoy ...... a picture used to trick birds

shatter .... break in small pieces

plumber ...... someone who works on water pipes

Read each passage. Then choose the correct answer for each question.

THE ROCK

Scoop and Skip were driving behind a big truck. Suddenly, an enormous rock fell off the truck. It fell in front of Scoop's car!

Scoop and Skip got out of the car. Some people came by to help them move it. They pushed it to the park. Now people sit on it.

1 The rock was—

A. in the car
B. at the park
C. on the truck
D. in the street

2 Scoop and Skip needed help to—

A. move the rock
B. stop the car
C. sit on the rock
D. drive the truck

THE NIGHT RIDE

Dave asked Meg to go on a boat cruise at night. "What can we see at night?" Meg said.

"You'll see," said Dave. When the boat left the dock, the sun was going down. Then they watched the lights in the city go on. The stars came out.

"This is a beautiful ride!" said Meg.

3 As the boat left the dock—

    A. the sun was rising
    B. the stars came out
    C. the sun went down
    D. the moon came out

4 From the boat, Meg saw—

    A. lots of fish
    B. a blue sky
    C. the sun come up
    D. city lights

A GOOD TRICK

Scoop's dog Scamp had a good trick. Each morning, he would go outside and bring the newspaper to the porch.

But one day Scoop opened the door. There were ten newspapers. Scamp had picked up all the newspapers on the block.

5 Scamp put the newspapers—

    A. on the porch
    B. on a box
    C. on the door
    D. on the bed

6 Scamp got ten newspapers from—

    A. the store
    B. the yard
    C. the neighborhood
    D. the porch

THE WINDOW

Meg's window was broken again. The window was by a tree where many birds lived. Almost every week a bird would fly into her window and shatter it.

Meg had an idea. She painted bird decoys on her window. Now the birds stay away from the window.

7 Meg's window is by a—

    A. park
    B. tree
    C. barn
    D. decoy

8 Meg's window was broken by—

    A. big stones
    B. baseballs
    C. decoys
    D. flying birds

FIX-IT DAY

Once a month, Dave's neighbors get together. They go from house to house, fixing things. Mr. Sims was a plumber. He worked on Dave's sink. Ms. Green fixed Mrs. Lopez's porch steps. The neighborhood looked great after fix-it day.

9 Mr. Sims was a—

    A. neighbor
    B. plumber
    C. carpenter
    D. toolmaker

10 Ms. Green fixed—

    A. some porch steps
    B. the plumbing
    C. the neighborhood
    D. Mr. Sims' house

Now use the Answer Key to check your answers. Mark the number you got correct on the Progress Chart.

LESSON 8

VOCABULARY

strain . . . . . work hard
destroyed . . broken up
arid . . . . . . dry

seldom . . . . . . not often
shield . . . . . . protect

Read each passage. Then choose the correct answer for each question.

THE CAVE

Scoop and Skip went exploring. They found a cave and walked a little way inside. It was dark, so Scoop went to get a flashlight. When he came back, the cave opening was closed! Some rocks had fallen and covered it. Skip was caught inside!

Scoop began to move the rocks. He used a big stick to move a very big rock. He had to strain to get it off. Finally, he reached Skip. He was all right.

Scoop and Skip still explore together, but they stay away from caves.

1 Scoop and Skip were exploring a—

A. rock
B. park
C. cave
D. lake

2 Scoop pushed away a big rock with—

A. a stick
B. his hands
C. a bat
D. a car

A BIG MESS

Meg was waiting to cross the street. She saw a van come out of the parking lot of a grocery store. It went around the corner very fast. Suddenly, the back of the van came undone. Five bags of groceries came out! Soon, there was food all over the street.

Meg waited until the traffic went by. Then she helped the driver pick up bread and apples and cheese. The eggs were destroyed. There was spilled milk and broken potato chips all over the road. What a mess!

3 The van was going around the corner—

A. very slow
B. very fast
C. backwards
D. sideways

4 The eggs and potato chips were—

A. in the van
B. in the store
C. broken
D. good to eat

CLEVER CAMEL

A desert is a very arid place. Rain seldom falls there. It might rain once in four years! The camel does well in its dry home. The camel can go for about eight days without water. Its feet are wide and have soft pads. They do not sink in the sand. The camel also has two sets of eyelashes on each eye. The eyelashes shield the camel's eyes from sand. The desert is the perfect place for the camel to live.

5 In the desert, rain falls—

   A. every day
   B. once a year
   C. every month
   D. every four years

6 Camels' feet are—

   A. very small
   B. too big
   C. very long
   D. very wide

7 Camels can go without water for—

   A. three days
   B. eight hours
   C. eight days
   D. one year

THE WORKSHOP

Skip liked to hang out at Mr. Lee's workshop. Mr. Lee could make almost anything. He made great furniture. He had built chairs or tables for almost everyone in the neighborhood. Skip really liked the chairs Mr. Lee made. They were very comfortable. One day Mr. Lee said, "It's time I made something for you, Skip. What would you like?"

"Oh, I'd like a chair, Mr. Lee," said Skip. "And I'd like to help you make it, too. I want to learn how to do woodworking."

8 Mr. Lee makes—

   A. toy animals
   B. furniture
   C. boxes
   D. houses

9 Skip liked Mr. Lee's—

   A. chairs
   B. house
   C. toys
   D. tools

10 Skip wanted to learn—

   A. how to get a job
   B. how to make a chair
   C. how to build a house
   D. how to make toys

Now use the Answer Key to check your answers. Mark the number you got correct on the Progress Chart.

LESSON 9

VOCABULARY

irritation . . . . . . soreness
produce . . . . make
sensitive . . . . . . easily hurt

rhythm . . . . the beats you can hear in a song
vibration . . . . a shaking

Read each passage. Then choose the correct answer for each question.

A GOOD CRY

Often we cry when we are sad. That doesn't feel very good. But crying tears is good for your eyes. Your eyes are very sensitive. They don't have much skin to protect them. Tears help clean out your eyes. Tears also have salt in them. That helps heal any irritation in the eyes.

Many other animals produce some kind of tears. Tears protect the eyes and keep them from getting dry. Whales have unusual tears. The tears have oil in them. The oily tears protect the whale's eyes from the salty sea.

Even if you don't like to cry, there is a good reason for it. So don't forget to shed a few tears.

1 Tears—

    A. clean out your eyes
    B. make you feel very sad
    C. are not good for you
    D. look very unusual

2 People's tears contain—

    A. fish
    B. oil
    C. sand
    D. salt

3 Whale tears contain—

    A. water
    B. sand
    C. oil
    D. salt

DANCING TO THE BEAT

What does it take to do a dance? Usually, you need to hear music. Then you move your body to the rhythm. But what if you could not hear?

There was a dancer named Mr. Fine. He had lost his hearing. At first, he did not know if he would dance again. But one day he visited a friend who played the drums. He played the drums very loud. Mr. Fine could feel the vibration from the sound. He started to dance to the beat.

Now Mr. Fine teaches other deaf people to dance. He turns the music up loud, and the dancers can move to the rhythms.

4 To dance, you need—

A. clothes
B. music
C. hearing
D. friends

5 Mr. Fine thought—

A. he might not dance again
B. he was a great dancer
C. he would learn to drum
D. he did not dance well

6 Mr. Fine could feel—

A. other people talking
B. very sad at times
C. the drum's vibrations
D. all kinds of sounds

UNUSUAL TREES

There are many kinds of trees in the world. Some of them are very unusual. There is a tree with lots of tiny gray leaves. They make a shape that looks like a big puff of smoke. It is called a smoke tree.

There is a tree called the traveler's tree. It has leaves that are shaped like cups. Water collects in the leaves. People often stop and drink water from the leaves. It is a very popular tree in some countries.

There is a tree that is not so popular. The branches of this tree grow out like vines. They wrap themselves around other trees and kill them!

7 The leaves of a smoke tree are—

A. grey
B. green
C. big
D. vines

8 A traveler's tree has—

A. tiny leaves
B. cup-shaped leaves
C. branches like vines
D. gray leaves

9 The traveler's tree is—

A. unpopular
B. very small
C. too big
D. popular

10 The strangler tree has—

A. cup-shaped leaves
B. branches like vines
C. very big leaves
D. tiny gray leaves

Now use the Answer Key to check your answers. Mark the number you got correct on the Progress Chart.

LESSON 10

VOCABULARY

Inuit . . . . . an Indian tribe in Alaska
challenge . . something hard to do
target . . . . . something to aim at
sonata . . . . a kind of song

composer . . . . . someone who writes music
constellation . . . a group of stars

Read each passage. Then choose the correct answer for each question.

A NEW FLAG

Ben lived in Alaska. He was a member of the Inuit (say IN•you•it) tribe. Ben's family had lived in Alaska before it became a state.

The year was 1959. Ben was at school one day. His teacher said there would be a contest. They wanted to find a picture to put on a flag. It would be the new flag for the state of Alaska. They asked children from all over the state to send pictures. Ben's class drew pictures for the contest.

Ben sat for a long time with his paper. He thought about Alaska. He loved the mountains and the forests. But Ben loved one thing best of all. He loved to look at the stars. He always looked for constellations in the sky. Suddenly, he knew what his picture would be. He made a drawing of the Big Dipper stars for his flag.

Ben's picture was picked for the flag! He was so proud. He got to march in a parade with the flag he had drawn. Everyone clapped for the new state flag.

1 Ben was a member of—

   A. the boy scouts
   B. the marching band
   C. the Inuit tribe
   D. Alaska

2 The contest was to draw—

   A. the best student
   B. the best picture
   C. the best flag
   D. the best school

3 Ben got to—

   A. go to the mountains
   B. go to a new school
   C. go to Alaska
   D. march in a parade

FRISBEE GOLF

You've probably played Frisbee before. It is a very popular game. Someone decided to make Frisbee more of a challenge. So Frisbee golf was invented.

For Frisbee golf, the first thing you do is set up a course. You pick a spot on a tree. You put a number or a basket on it. This becomes a target for your Frisbee. Set up several targets.

Then you take turns throwing your Frisbee. You try to hit the target or basket. Sometimes, it is hard to throw that far. Or a tree gets in the way. That is part of the fun.

4 You play Frisbee golf—

A. outside
B. in a gym
C. in the pool
D. inside

5 For a golf team, you need—

A. twenty Frisbees
B. several targets
C. one target
D. five trees

6 In Frisbee golf—

A. you try to hit the target
B. you throw it for your dog
C. you throw it from a car
D. you throw it inside

THE SONG IN THE NIGHT

Ludwig van Beethoven (say BAY•toe•ven) was a great composer. One night he was out walking. There was a full moon. Suddenly he heard a song. It was a song that he wrote! It was coming from a little house. He listened to it. Then it stopped, and he heard someone crying.

Beethoven knocked on the door. Inside, a young girl was sitting at the piano. "I will never learn to play this song!" she cried. "I cannot pay for lessons. I wish I knew how it should sound!"

Beethoven walked to the piano. There was no sheet music. He saw that the girl was blind. Beethoven played the song for the girl. She thanked him for his kindness. That night, he went home and wrote a new song. It was called Moonlight Sonata.

Later in his life, Beethoven became deaf. But he kept writing music. Maybe he thought of the blind girl who would not give up.

7 In the story, Beethoven was walking—

A. at nighttime
B. by the ocean
C. in the morning
D. in the mountains

8 Beethoven heard his song coming—

A. from a big house
B. from a little house
C. from his house
D. from the street

9 The little girl was—

A. deaf
B. happy
C. blind
D. asleep

10 Beethoven went home and wrote—

A. a letter
B. a book
C. a poem
D. a song

Now use the Answer Key to check your answers. Mark the number you got correct on the Progress Chart.

LESSON 11

VOCABULARY

temperature . how hot or cold it is
scientists . . . . people who study science
surface . . . . . top of the land
blizzards . . . snow storms

endure . . . . to live through something hard
material . . . what something is made of

Read each passage. Then choose the correct answer for each question.

LIFE AT THE SOUTH POLE

The South Pole is at the bottom of the earth. It is a very cold place. The land is completely covered with ice. No plants grow there. There are very few animals.

People could not survive on the land of the South Pole. They would freeze to death!

The temperature goes down to 80 degrees below zero. The winds are also very strong. The snow blows and covers buildings. It can blind people quickly. They can easily get lost and die.

Scientists found a way to live at the South Pole. They dug into the snow and ice. They built a city underground where people can stay warmer. They are protected from the wind. The scientists have made their city a very nice place. Each person has a private room. Tunnels connect the rooms. They have good food to eat. They have an exercise gym. They even have a movie theater!

Every day, the scientists go up to the surface. They study the land. It is very dangerous. Blizzards can sneak up suddenly.

They could get lost in the snow. They use ropes to find their way back to the door.

In the winter, the sun does not come up at all. The scientists do their work in the dark. When summer comes, most people leave the South Pole city. Usually, one winter is all they can endure.

1 The South Pole is—

   A. warm
   B. cold
   C. ugly
   D. new

2 The city on the South Pole is—

   A. very big
   B. very old
   C. on a hill
   D. underground

3 The city has—

   A. roads
   B. skyscrapers
   C. tunnels
   D. cars

4 The scientists study—

    A. the land
    B. the city
    C. exercise
    D. the movies

5 At the South Pole, winter—

    A. is time to go outside
    B. is always dark
    C. is very warm
    D. is always light

NO PLACE LIKE HOME

Birds do not always make their nests in trees. They don't always live in birdhouses. Sometimes, you will find bird nests in strange places.

Some birds have made homes in mailboxes. Sometimes mail carriers will find nests when they put letters in the box.

Sometimes people give birds a place for a nest. Once a boy went to look for his baseball glove. There was a bird nesting in it! He left it up on its hook that year. The birds had a cozy spot to live in.

Once a man went to get his suit. It had been left out on the wash line. A bird had made a nest right in the pocket! Another bird made its nest inside an old tin can. Once they found a bird nest on top of a train! The birds got a free ride. But it must have been hard to hang on!

Usually we think of a bird nest being made of sticks and mud. But birds use all kinds of materials to make their nests. One nest had a bubble gum wrapper in it.

Another bird found a dollar bill. It was used to line the nest.

Birds sometimes build very creative nests. But they always try to make a warm, safe home for their families.

6 Bird nests are often made of—

    A. sticks and mud
    B. bubble gum
    C. letters
    D. old tin cans

7 Some birds make a home in—

    A. a dog house
    B. a street
    C. a mailbox
    D. a letter

8 One bird nest was found—

    A. in a baseball glove
    B. under a train
    C. in a shoebox
    D. on the street

9 One bird lined its nest with—

    A. pennies
    B. a dollar bill
    C. a glove
    D. bubble gum

10 Birds always make nests that are—

    A. very unusual
    B. very pretty
    C. not in good places
    D. safe and warm

Now use the Answer Key to check your answers. Mark the number you got correct on the Progress Chart.

LESSON 12

VOCABULARY

dedicate . . . give yourself to something

preserving . . saving

Indiana . . . . a state in the middle of America

California . . a state on the West Coast of America

champion . . . . someone who fights for something

environment . . the land and animals

appreciate . . . to understand something is important

Read the passage. It is an article about John Muir. He was a great lover of nature. Then choose the correct answer for each question.

JOHN MUIR

John Muir came to America when he was 11 years old. He and his family moved to a farm. All day, he worked in the fields. But he would also find time to explore the woods. He loved to be outdoors.

One day, he was playing with his friends. He saw something move up in a tree. It was a little bird. It was alone in a nest. John decided that he wanted the bird for a pet. He carefully climbed the tree. Then he put the bird in his pocket and took it home.

He tried to take good care of his bird. He got food and water for it. He put it in a big cage by the window. But the bird was not happy. It just sat in its cage. Only once a day did the bird seem happy at all. When the sun came up it would fly to the top of its cage and sing a sweet song.

This song should have made John happy. But it made him very sad. A voice inside his head said, "Let the bird go! Let it go!" Finally, John knew what he had to do. He let the bird go.

After that, John knew he could never again keep an animal in a cage. He also knew something important about himself. He wanted to help save animals and their homes. He wanted to dedicate his life to preserving nature.

That's just what John did for the rest of his life. After he grew up, he walked over 1,000 miles, from Indiana to California. John climbed mountains and went down rivers. He learned all about America's beautiful land. And he fought to keep humans from destroying nature.

John Muir was America's first great champion for the environment. He wrote about the beauty of the natural world. He made people stop and think about the land. He taught people to appreciate the world around them. And you could say that he learned it all from a little bird.

Identifying the Sequence

1 When did John Muir live on a farm?

   A. Before he came to America.
   B. After he came to America.
   C. After he found the bird.
   D. Before he was born.

2 When did John Muir put the bird in a cage?

   A. After he hiked 1,000 miles.
   B. Before he came to America.
   C. After he found it in the tree.
   D. When he was grown up.

3 When did John walk 1,000 miles?

   A. After he grew up.
   B. When he was young.
   C. Before he let the bird go.
   D. Before he came to America.

4 When did John write about nature?

   A. Before hc came to America.
   B. When he was young.
   C. Before he lived on a farm.
   D. After he saw America's land.

Identifying Details

5 In the tree, John saw—

   A. a bird
   B. a squirrel
   C. other boys
   D. some fruit

6 John decided he wanted—

   A. to play games
   B. to go to school
   C. to chase birds
   D. to have a pet bird

7 John gave the bird—

   A. a nest
   B. songs to sing
   C. food and water
   D. a tree

8 The bird was—

   A. happy
   B. busy
   C. mean
   D. sad

9 John knew he had to—

   A. get another bird
   B. let the bird go
   C. keep the bird
   D. get new bird food

10 John wrote about—

   A. birds and cages
   B. life on a farm
   C. life in America
   D. the beauty of nature

Now use the Answer Key to check your answers. Mark the number you got correct on the Progress Chart.

UNIT 3
LESSON 13

Skill Focus: Understanding the Main Idea

It is important to find the Main Idea of what you are reading. The main idea is what the selection is mostly about. Here are some clues to help you:

- Read carefully.
- Look for a sentence that tells what the selection is mostly about.
- Add up the important details.
- Look for words that are used often.
- Think what would make a good title for the selection.

VOCABULARY

comedy . . . . things that are funny
puncture . . . a rip or tear

gentle . . . . . . nice
extends . . . . . is as long as

Read each passage. Then choose the correct answer for each question.

Doctors say it's good for people to laugh. It can help sick people feel better.

One man was very sick. He decided to rent comedy movies. His friends came over and told jokes. Soon the man got better. Why? No one knows for sure.

1 What is the main idea?

   A. You smile when you are not mad.
   B. Laughing can help you feel better.
   C. It is fun to makes jokes all the time.
   D. Doctors are very funny.

2 What would be a good title?

   A. Laughing is Good for You
   B. Funny Movies
   C. How to Laugh
   D. Funny Doctors

Skip got a new dog named Scooby. Scooby didn't look like a dog. He looked like a wolf. But Scooby was only part wolf. He was very gentle. The only time he acted like a wolf was when he wanted to play. Then he would howl like this: "OWWW-owww."

3 What is the main idea?

A. Scooby was a very big dog.
B. Scooby looked like a wolf, but didn't act like one.
C. Skip bought a small dog.
D. Skip decided he did not like dogs.

4 What would be a good title?

A. Scooby the Wolf Dog
B. How to Pick a Dog
C. A Wolf in the Wild
D. Scooby Likes to Play

Scoop's car started to shake. Scoop stopped the car and got out. The tire had a puncture in it. "I will have to put on a new tire," said Scoop. Soon the new tire was on. Away Scoop went.

5 What is the main idea?

A. Scoop needs a new car.
B. Scoop gave his car away.
C. Scoop did not drive well.
D. Scoop put on a new tire.

6 What is a good title?

A. Scoop's Car
B. The New Car
C. The Flat Tire
D. How to Fix a Flat

Have you ever seen a bike for two riders? There are also bikes for three riders. There is one bike that is even longer. It extends as long as twelve bikes put together! More than thirty people are needed to ride it!

7 What is the main idea?

A. There are bikes for three riders.
B. One person can ride a very long bike.
C. One bike is as long as twelve bikes put together.
D. Bikes are not much fun to ride.

8 What is a good title?

A. Riding Your Bike
B. A Bike for Two
C. A Bike for Three
D. The Longest Bike

Rock climbers wear special climbing shoes. The shoes are too tight. This is so the foot will not slip. The climbers hook their ropes together. That helps them stay safe. Rock climbers must be very careful. They do not hurry but take their time.

9 What is the main idea?

A. Some rocks are bigger than others.
B. Rock climbers have to be careful.
C. Rock climbers are always in a hurry.
D. Climbing shoes are very tight.

10 What is a good title?

A. Climbing Shoes
B. Hurry to the Top
C. Ropes and Hooks
D. Rock Climbing

Now use the Answer Key to check your answers. Mark the number you got correct on the Progress Chart.

LESSON 14

VOCABULARY

deposits · · · holes in the earth filled with something

delivers · · · · brings to someone

handsome · · · · good-looking

wrinkles · · · · · folds in the skin

Read each passage. Then choose the correct answer for each question.

Meg was staying by a big lake for the summer. One day, a man drove up in a car. The man asked, "Do you have any worms? I want to go fishing." Meg said she did not have any worms. But Meg got to thinking. She decided to dig up some worms.

The next day, Meg sold worms. Lots of cars stopped. She made ten dollars that day! Meg decided she would sell worms all summer.

1 What is the main idea?

   A. Meg did not like worms.
   B. Meg found a summer job.
   C. Meg liked the lake.
   D. Meg wanted to go fishing.

2 What is the best title?

   A. Meg Goes Fishing
   B. A Beautiful Lake
   C. Meg Likes Worms
   D. A Good Idea

Earth is a very salty planet. There is salt in the ocean. There are salt deposits in the ground. There is also salt inside of you. Your blood has salt in it. Your sweat is salty. There is even salt in your tears.

Why is there so much salt around? Much of Earth used to be underwater. When the oceans got smaller, salt was left behind. It's a good thing, too. People cannot live without salt.

3 What is the main idea?

   A. There is salt in your tears.
   B. There is a lot of salt on Earth.
   C. Salt is very bad for people.
   D. People use salt for many things.

4 What would be a good title?

   A. Salt in the Ocean
   B. Salt in Our Blood
   C. The Salty Planet
   D. Salty Tears

Carla has a very unusual job. She delivers newspapers. Lots of people have that job. They ride a bike. They go through the neighborhood. They put a newspaper by each door.

Carla does things differently. She lives on a mountain. People live far apart. So Carla rides her horse on the job. She can get around much better that way.

Carla likes her job. She also likes riding her horse every day.

5 What is the main idea?

   A. Carla has an unusual job.
   B. Carla likes to have a job.
   C. Carla likes her horse.
   D. Carla doesn't like horses.

6 What is the main idea of the last paragraph?

   A. Carla delivers newspapers.
   B. Carla likes her job.
   C. Carla likes her horse.
   D. Carla has a job.

7 What would be a good title?

   A. Writing for the Newspaper
   B. What Horses Like for Dinner
   C. Carla's Unusual Job
   D. How to Get a Job

Maybe you have a pet dog. Is your dog cute? Sometimes, people will put handsome dogs in a contest. The best-looking animal wins.

There is another kind of dog contest. It is called the "Ugly Dog Contest." People bring all sorts of dogs. Some of them are very hairy. Some have no hair at all. Some dogs have big wrinkles. The ugliest dog wins the prize.

People love their ugly dogs just as much as a cute dog. Being ugly makes the dogs kind of special!

8 What is the main idea?

   A. There are contests for ugly dogs.
   B. There are contests for cute dogs.
   C. Some dogs like to go to contests.
   D. Most dogs are cute.

9 What is the main idea of the last paragraph.

   A. People don't like ugly dogs.
   B. People like to be in contests.
   C. Some dogs are too ugly.
   D. Ugly dogs are kind of special.

10 What is a good title?

   A. A Cute Dog Contest
   B. How to Get a Dog
   C. An Ugly Dog Contest
   D. Who Has the Best Dog?

Now use the Answer Key to check your answers. Mark the number you got correct on the Progress Chart.

UNIT 3
LESSON 15
VOCABULARY

patterns . . . shapes that repeat
Mexico . . . . a country south of the United States

spectacle . . . a great sight
mystery . . . . something that is not known
active . . . . . does many things

Read each passage. Then choose the correct answer for each question.

There are trees that walk. Believe it or not, it is true! The trees are in Florida. Florida is a very warm place. It gets a lot of rain. The trees grow in the muddy salt water. They are very hardy.

The walking trees have long roots. The roots reach way out and drop in the mud. When the root reaches out, it pulls the tree along. That is how the trees "walk."

Fish live around the roots of the trees. They don't have to worry about getting stepped on. It takes a tree one year to move ten feet.

1 What is the main idea?

A. Florida is a warm place.
B. Fish like the walking tree.
C. There are trees that walk.
D. Trees have roots.

2 What is the main idea of the last paragraph?

A. The walking tree is tall.
B. The walking tree moves slowly.
C. Fish live in the water.
D. The trees have very long roots.

3 What would be a good title?

A. Trees in Florida
B. Trees that Walk
C. Fish in Florida
D. Fish That Like Trees

Monarch butterflies are beautiful. They are bright orange with black patterns. They are also very smart.

Every spring, the Monarchs wake up. They have been sleeping all winter. Every year the Monarchs do the same thing. They fly far away to Mexico.

All the Monarchs go to the same place. They swarm onto the branches of trees. The trees start to look like big butterflies. It is quite a spectacle.

How do the Monarchs know where to go? Maybe they follow the scent of other Monarchs. But no one really knows for sure. It is a mystery.

4 What is the main idea?

   A. Monarch butterflies go to the same place each year.
   B. The butterflies live on tree branches.
   C. Monarch butterflies always get lost.
   D. Monarch butterflies are beautiful.

5 What is the main idea of the last paragraph?

   A. Monarch butterflies are beautiful.
   B. No one knows why Monarchs go to Mexico.
   C. Monarchs like to swarm onto trees.
   D. Monarchs can smell other butterflies.

6 What would be a good title?

   A. The Monarchs in Mexico
   B. Smelly Butterflies
   C. The Beautiful Monarchs
   D. Mystery of the Monarchs

There was a boy named George Phillips. He was born with no eyesight. Even so, George was very active. He loved to swim. He also sailed his own boat.

One day, George was at the beach. Suddenly, he heard someone cry for help. It was coming from the water. He asked his friends if they heard anything. They looked out at the water. They couldn't see anything wrong.

George was the only one who could hear the sound. He jumped in his boat. He rowed toward the sound. George found a woman in the water. He pulled her into the boat. George's sharp ears saved the day!

7 What is the main idea?

   A. George could sail and swim very well.
   B. George's good hearing saved the day.
   C. George liked to go to the beach.
   D. George's friends could not hear well.

8 What is the main idea of the first paragraph?

   A. George could swim well.
   B. George could sail well.
   C. George was very active.
   D. George had his own boat.

9 What is the main idea of the last paragraph?

   A. George's friends could not hear the cry for help.
   B. George's friends did not like going to the beach.
   C. The beach is a scary place to go for a swim.
   D. George saved a woman in the water.

10 What is a good title?

   A. George Saves the Day
   B. George Can't See
   C. George has Good Hearing
   D. George Likes the Beach

Now use the Answer Key to check your answers. Mark the number you got correct on the Progress Chart.

LESSON 16

VOCABULARY

colony . . . . . a group that lives together
scamper . . . run fast
portable . . . something you can take with you

annoyed . . . . . made upset
paralyzed . . . . cannot move
method . . . . . a way of doing something

Read each passage. Then choose the correct answer for each question.

There is a park in California. In that park lives a colony of lizards. Every spring, the lizards would travel to a special spot. They would lay their eggs there.

There was a problem with the lizards. They had to cross a road to get to their special spot. Often cars would run over the little lizards. The lizards were starting to die out.

People decided that something had to be done. They got some volunteers together. In the spring, they would take turns standing by the road. When a lizard came up, they would stop the cars. Then the lizard would scamper across.

Some drivers were a little annoyed with this plan. But most understood how important it was to save the lizards.

1 What is the main idea?

   A. People worked to save the lizards.
   B. Most people do not like lizards.
   C. There are too many cars.
   D. The lizards should move away.

2 What is the main idea of the second paragraph?

   A. People drive too fast.
   B. The lizards run too slow.
   C. There were lots of cars on the road.
   D. The lizards were dying out.

3 What is a good title?

   A. Do You Like Lizards?
   B. People Like Parks
   C. Too Much Traffic
   D. Save the Lizards!

Have you played Hacky-Sack before? All you need is a tiny leather ball. You just have to keep the ball up in the air. Sound easy? It isn't!

It is pretty easy to kick a football or a soccer ball. In Hacky-Sack, the ball is tiny. You have to move your foot or leg quickly. You can't hit the ball with your heel or your toe. You can catch it with your knee. But you can't let the ball drop.

You have probably seen people playing Hacky-Sack by themselves or with one other person. You can do it anywhere. You can carry the ball in your pocket. It is a very portable sport. It is also a lot of fun!

4 What is the main idea?

A. Hacky-Sack is not fun.
B. Hacky-Sack is very easy.
C. Hacky-Sack is hard to play.
D. Hacky-Sack is a new game.

5 What is the main idea of the last paragraph?

A. People play Hacky-Sack in the park.
B. Hacky-Sack is very easy to play.
C. You can play Hacky-Sack anywhere.
D. Most people aren't good at Hacky-Sack.

6 What would be a good title?

A. An Easy Game
B. All About Hacky-Sack
C. How to Play Soccer
D. How to Play Football

Horace Pippin wanted to study art. But he lived in small town. There were no art classes open to African Americans. So Pippin taught himself how to paint.

Pippin fought in World War I. Then something happened that changed his life. His right arm became paralyzed. Pippin could no longer paint.

Pippin did not let this stop him. He kept trying new methods. One day he held a hot poker between his arm and knee. He burned shapes into a flat board. These shapes held the paint longer. That gave Pippin a chance to paint slowly.

People like Pippin's paintings. They are very simple. But they are also very powerful. He shows scenes from his life. Horace Pippin's work tells a lot about being African American.

7 What is the main idea?

A. Horace Pippin fought in a war.
B. Horace Pippin was paralyzed.
C. Horace Pippin worked hard to become an artist.
D. Horace Pippen was a good painter.

8 What is the main idea of the first paragraph?

A. Pippin taught himself how to paint.
B. Pippin fought in World War I.
C. Pippen lived in a small town.
D. Pippin used a hot poker to paint.

9 What is the main idea of the last paragraph?

A. Pippen had very simple paintings.
B. Pippin's work tells about being African American.
C. Pippin used a hot poker to paint.
D. Horace Pippin became a very famous painter.

10 What would be a good title?

A. Simple Paintings
B. Learning to Paint
C. The Art of Horace Pippin
D. The Art of World War I

Now use the Answer Key to check your answers. Mark the number you got correct on the Progress Chart.

LESSON 17

VOCABULARY

Europeans ..	people who came from Europe	**culture** ...	people's songs, stories, and arts
predator ...	an animal that will kill another animal	**modern** ..	of today
		partners ..	two who work together
		guide	to lead

Read each passage. Then choose the correct answer for each question.

For many years, the Inuit people lived in Northwest Canada. It was a hard life. But they knew how to make it work. They knew how to hunt and fish. They could make a living on the land.

When Europeans came, the Inuits lost the land. The people could not do the work they had always done. It caused many problems. The Inuit culture almost died.

On April 1, 1999, everything changed. The Inuit people got their land back. A new country was born. They named their country Nunavet (say NOON•a•vet). That means "our land." The Inuits will decide how to run their country.

The people of Ninavet want to bring back things from the past. They want young people to know where they came from. But they also want to be a modern country. They want to have jobs that will help Ninavet be successful.

The people of Ninavet have many hopes and dreams. And they have the freedom to make their country a very special place.

1 What is the main idea?

  A. The Inuits have to build a new country.
  B. The Inuits don't fish.
  C. The people of Ninavet want to go hunting and fishing.
  D. Ninavet is in Canada.

2 What is the main idea of the second paragraph?

  A. The Inuit people hunt and fish.
  B. The Inuit people lost their land to the Europeans.
  C. The Inuit people don't hunt or fish.
  D. The Inuit people were from Ninavet.

3 What is the main idea of the third paragraph?

  A. In 1999, the Inuit lived in Northwest Canada.
  B. In 1999, the Inuit lost Ninavet.
  C. In 1899, Ninavet became a country.
  D. In 1999, Ninavet became a country.

4 What is the main idea of the last paragraph?

A. The people of Ninavet can hunt.
B. Ninavet has the freedom to choose.
C. Ninavet does not know what to do.
D. The Inuits have few hopes.

5 What would be a good title?

A. Northwest Canada
B. The Inuit People
C. A New Country
D. Living in Canada

Many animals are not too friendly with each other. Someone could get eaten that way! But some animals become partners. They help each other out.

There are birds called oxpeckers. They ride on the back of the water buffalo. They peck the bugs off the buffalo's skin. The oxpecker pecks at the buffalo's head when danger is coming. What does the oxpecker get for its trouble? It gets a home and lots of food.

There is a bird called a honey guide. It helps the honey badger (say BA•jer). Both of them like to find beehives. The bird flies around looking for a hive. When it finds one, it gets the badger. The badger breaks open the hive. Then they share the honey.

There are two animals that are partners. The impala is a deer. The baboon is a big, strong monkey. Impalas and baboons will go to a waterhole together. The impala can hear very well. It can warn the baboon when danger is coming. The baboon can

fight any predator that comes along. These two partners help keep each other safe.

6 What is the main idea?

A. Some animals don't like each other.
B. Some animals are in a lot of danger.
C. Some animals work well together.
D. Most animals have a partner.

7 What is the main idea of the first paragraph?

A. Many animals are not friendly.
B. Many animals do not know how to help each other.
C. Many animals could get eaten.
D. Many animals are in danger.

8 What is the main idea of the third paragraph?

A. The birds look for a hive.
B. Birds and badgers don't get along.
C. Badgers like sweets.
D. Birds and badgers help each other.

9 What is the main idea of the last paragraph?

A. The baboon likes to drink water.
B. The baboon and the impala are good partners.
C. The baboon is strong.
D. The impala can hear very well.

10 What would be a good title?

A. Baboons and Impalas
B. Wild Animals
C. Partners in Nature
D. Badgers Like Sweets

Now use the Answer Key to check your answers. Mark the number you got correct on the Progress Chart.

UNIT 3 REVIEW
LESSON 18
VOCABULARY

pondered . . . to think to yourself
brilliant . . . very bright
treasure . . . something worth a lot

tumbled . . . . . fell down
tending . . . . . taking care of
cautiously . . . . carefully

Read the passage. It is a folktale from Mexico. It tells a story about how corn got to be yellow. Then choose the correct answer for each question.

Long ago, corn was not yellow. It was blue. There was a farmer named Martin. He loved the sun. He would get up to watch it rise. He loved everything about it. He loved the gold glow. He loved the heat. Martin would watch the sun shine on his field of blue corn.

Martin worked all day. All day, he kept an eye on the sun. He watched when the sun went behind the clouds. He watched when he rested at noon.

At night, Martin watched the sun go down. "Where does it go?" he pondered. "Someday, I want to find out."

One day, Martin decided to follow the sun. He walked and walked. He followed it until he got to the sea. Then he saw the sun finally go down. It sank into the blue ocean. The sun gave off a brilliant flame. It lit the water and made it flash.

"So that is where the sun goes," said Martin. "Each night it gives the sea a blanket of gold."

Martin sat in the dark, thinking. He thought about the sun. He thought about the beautiful gold. He thought he would like to have a bit of gold for himself! "Perhaps I will take just a little," he said to himself.

Martin got some pails. Then he dipped them into the sea. The buckets were full of the sun's gold. He hurried off with his treasure.

He traveled all night to get home. He walked cautiously over the hills and through the fields. At last, he saw his farm in the distance. He had only one more hill to climb. Up, up he went in the black night.

But just as he reached the top, Martin fell! The pails tumbled down the hill. And the gold flowed over Martin's cornfield.

"I have lost the gold!" cried Martin, "It serves me right for trying to take it."

Martin was sad. But he had learned his lesson. He went back to tending his field.

Soon the corn was ripe. It was time for Martin to pick it. What a surprise he had. When he opened that first ear of corn, it was not blue. It was a golden yellow!

Martin smiled to himself. He knew what had happened. He remembered the pails of gold that he had spilled. And that is how the corn became yellow like the sun.

Identifying the Sequence

1 What happened first?

   A. Martin followed the sun.
   B. Martin was sad.
   C. Martin wanted some gold.
   D. Martin lost the gold.

2 What happened next?

   A. Martin followed the sun.
   B. Martin liked watching the sun.
   C. Martin wanted some gold.
   D. Martin picked his corn.

3 What happened last?

   A. Martin wanted some gold.
   B. Martin picked his corn.
   C. Martin spilled the pails.
   D. The corn came up gold.

Identifying Details

4 At the beginning of the story, corn was—

   A. green
   B. dark
   C. blue
   D. gold

5 Martin followed the sun—

   A. to his field
   B. up a big hill
   C. down a hill
   D. to the ocean

6 Martin wanted—

   A. to sell his corn
   B. to get some gold
   C. to buy a farm
   D. to sit in the sun

Understanding the Main Idea

7 What is the main idea of the story?

   A. Martin was greedy for gold.
   B. Corn got its gold from the sun.
   C. Corn does not need water.
   D. Corn has always been yellow.

8 What is the main idea of the first paragraph?

   A. Martin was greedy for gold.
   B. Martin loved to be a farmer.
   C. Martin loved the sun.
   D. Martin liked to walk.

9 What is the main idea of the last paragraph?

   A. Martin knew why the corn was gold.
   B. The corn was a golden yellow.
   C. Martin didn't know what had happened.
   D. Martin was sorry for what he had done.

10 What is a good title?

   A. Martin Finds Gold
   B. Why Corn is Blue
   C. Why Corn is Yellow
   D. How to Grow Corn

Now use the Answer Key to check your answers. Mark the number you got correct on the Progress Chart.

Skill Focus: Using the Context

You can learn to use the context to help you understand a difficult new word. Here are some clues to help you:

- Read the word carefully.
- Think about the meanings of other words in that sentence.
- Look at the sentences before and after.
- Look for an example sentence. It might give the meaning of the word in another way.

VOCABULARY

blossoms . . . . . flowers
disappointed . . feeling let down

seldom . . . . . . not often
squealing . . . . a high, loud sound

Read each passage. Then choose the correct word to fill in the blank.

NIGHT FLOWERS

Some flowers bloom after the (1)_____ goes down. They are called night flowers. The blossoms are yellow, pink, and white. They look very pretty until (2)_____. But when the sun comes up, they close up. They go to sleep for the day.

Look back at the passage. Choose the correct word to fill in the blank.

1 A. sun   C. flower
   B. cloud   D. moon

2 A. midnight   C. night
   B. lunchtime   D. morning

LOST

Meg went for a hike. She started in the afternoon. She (3)_____ a long way. Soon it was night. Meg realized that she was (4)_____. How could she get back to the house? Then she saw a light. Who could it be? She was ready to run. It was Dave. He had been looking for her.

Look back at the passage. Choose the correct word to fill in the blank.

3 A. flew   C. hiked
   B. skated   D. ran

4 A. lost   C. bored
   B. funny   D. home

THE WIND

There was a big (5)_____. The wind blew and blew. It blew against Jack's apple trees. Soon, the apples started to fall off. When the storm was over, Jack and Kit went outside. Jack was very disappointed. All of his (6)_____ were on the ground. Kit said, "It's okay, Jack. We'll make a lot of apple pies!"

Look back at the passage. Choose the correct word to fill in the blank.

5 A. party   C. field
   B. storm   D. wave

6 A. apples   C. friends
   B. trees   D. rain

GIRAFFES

Have you ever heard a giraffe make noise? Most people have not. Giraffes seldom make (7)_____. They do not "talk" to each other. But when it is hurt, a giraffe will make a "moo" sound. It sounds a little like a (8)_____. Giraffes also make noise when they are scared. They make a squealing sound.

Look back at the passage. Choose the correct word to fill in the blank.

7 A. food   C. noise
   B. scared   D. people

8 A. horse   C. foot
   B. storm   D. cow

A RAINY DAY

It was raining outside. There was nothing to do. Meg and Kate sat in a big room, looking out the window. "What shall we do?" asked Kate. "I am so bored."

"Look up at the walls," said Meg. "I see what we can do." The (9)_____ had lots of bookshelves. Meg picked out a book. It was about boats. Kate found a (10)_____ about horses. They read all afternoon.

Look back at the passage. Choose the correct word to fill in the blank.

9 A. rain   C. horses
   B. walls   D. boats

10 A. movie   C. book
   B. storm   D. boat

Now use the Answer Key to check your answers. Mark the number you got correct on the Progress Chart.

LESSON 20

VOCABULARY

bloated . . . . . filled too full	**cautiously** . . . . . very carefully	
antique . . . . . something very old	**damage** . . . . . . to hurt	

Read each passage. Then choose the correct word to fill in the blank.

WAKE UP!

Every night the same thing happens. Jan starts to yawn. She rubs her eyes. But she wants to stay up just a little longer.

Every morning, Jan's mother tries to (1)_____ her. Jan covers her face with the blanket. She goes back to sleep. Her mother calls her again. Still Jan doesn't move.

Finally, the dog comes in. He (2)_____ up on the bed and licks Jan's face. Then Jan has no choice. She has to get up!

Look back at the passage. Choose the correct word to fill in the blank.

1 A. catch   C. tickle
  B. yawn   D. wake

2 A. jumps   C. fly
  B. sleeps   D. runs

THE PET GOLDFISH

Skip went to the pet shop. He spoke to Mr. James. "My goldfish, Scamp, is sick," Skip said. "He is bloated. And he is swimming very slowly."

"How often do you feed your fish?" asked Mr. James.

"Scamp loves to eat. So I (3)_____ him four or five times a day. He eats every bite of it," said Skip.

"That's the problem!" said Mr. James. "That (4)_____ is eating way too much. Only feed your fish once a day. He'll feel better soon."

Look back at the passage. Choose the correct word to fill in the blank.

3 A. swim   C. feed
  B. run   D. catch

4 A. Skip   C. cat
  B. fish   D. James

THE SCRAPBOOK

Meg and her grandma were looking at a scrapbook. There were pictures of her grandma and grandpa when they were young. They stood by an antique car. "Where did you get that old (5) _____,

Grandma?" asked Meg.

"That was our first car," said Grandma. "It was new when we got it."

Then Meg looked at a (6)_____ of a funny-looking baby. "Who is that baby?" asked Meg.

"Can't you guess?" said Grandma. "That (7)_____ is you!"

Look back at the passage. Choose the correct word to fill in the blank.

5 A. car   C. picture
   B. cat   D. grandpa

6 A. movie   C. car
   B. picture   D. scrapbook

7 A. car   C. baby
   B. Grandma   D. funny

THE CAR WASH

Skip took Scoop's car to the car wash. He drove there very cautiously. He did not want to damage Scoop's (8)_____.

When Skip got to the car wash, he paid his (9)_____. He got the car in the right place. He drove it into the washing machine.

Suddenly, Skip looked in the back seat. The window was open a crack! The (10)_____ was spraying on the back seat. It took Skip all afternoon to get the water mopped up.

Look back at the passage. Choose the correct word to fill in the blank.

8 A. pet   C. cat
   B. wash   D. car

9 A. money   C. car
   B. wet   D. cat

10 A. sun   C. mop
   B. water   D. car

Now use the Answer Key to check your answers. Mark the number you got correct on the Progress Chart.

VOCABULARY

factory . . . . a place where they make things

successful . . does well

peculiar . . . . . unusual

steer . . . . a male cow

Read each passage. Then choose the correct word to fill in the blank.

JELLY BELLIES

Jelly beans have been around for a long time. Most children like to (1)_____ them. A man named David Klein (say kline) ran a candy factory. He made jelly beans. His company was pretty successful.

One day, David had an idea. He thought that he would make jelly beans that grown-ups would like. He made some jelly beans with peculiar flavors. He made some with watermelon and coconut (2)_____. Then he tried them out on his friends. Everyone thought they were great. His friends called David "Mr. Jelly Belly."

David made more flavors for his jelly beans. Now you can get Jelly Bellies that (3)_____ like baked apple, root beer, and even buttered popcorn!

Look back at the passage. Choose the correct word to fill in the blank.

1   A. jelly   C. wash
    B. eat   D. see

2   A. flavors   C. colors
    B. shapes   D. ideas

3   A. look   C. run
    B. flavor   D. taste

BILL PICKETT

Rodeos are shows with cowboys, horses, and bulls. Rodeos were once very popular. The cowboys rode the horses. Sometimes they tried to catch bulls.

The best rodeo cowboy ever was an African-American. His name was Bill Pickett. He lived over a hundred years ago. Bill always worked with horses. He would (4)_____ steers that ran away. One day, an angry steer ran off. Bill went after it. He jumped onto the steer's back. He put a rope around its neck. Then he jumped off. He pulled the (5)_____ and the steer stopped.

Bill did this trick in many rodeos. They called it "bulldogging." Lots of (6)_____ tried bulldogging. But no one was ever as good as Bill Pickett.

Look back at the passage. Choose the correct word to fill in the blank.

4   A. sleep   C. chase
   B. hit   D. run

5   A. rodeo   C. chase
   B. rope   D. cowboy

6   A. steers   C. cowboys
   B. rodeo   D. bulls

THE ROPE-JUMPING CHAMPS

One winter, it was very cold. It stayed cold for many weeks. Mr. Reiser's students could not go outdoors for recess. They had to play (7)_____. Mr. Reiser had an idea. He got a lot of jump ropes. He gave them to the students to play with. They (8)_____ rope every day. Soon they got very good at it.

 Mr. Reiser said, "Let's see how many kids can jump at one time." They got a very long (9)_____. First, ten kids jumped the rope. Every day, they would (10)_____ more kids. Finally, 51 students jumped the rope together. They had become the best rope-jumpers in the world!

Look back at the passage. Choose the correct word to fill in the blank.

7   A. inside   C. upstairs
   B. outside   D. alone

8   A. cut   C. jumped
   B. threw   D. made

9   A. cold   C. recess
   B. jump   D. rope

10   A. forget   C. chase
    B. add   D. play

Now use the Answer Key to check your answers. Mark the number you got correct on the Progress Chart.

LESSON 22

VOCABULARY

creatures . . . living things
theory . . . . . idea
meteor . . . . a rock from outer space
history . . . . stories about the past

Georgia . . . . . a state in the southern United States
sturdy . . . . . . strong

Read each passage. Then choose the correct word to fill in the blank.

WHERE DID THEY GO?

You have probably read about dinosaurs. They lived on Earth a long time ago. We know what these creatures looked like. Some were very big. Some had wings. Many could swim. Some of them ate (1)_____. Others ate only vegetables.

Then the dinosaurs died off. That is the part we do not know about. Why did they disappear? One theory is that sickness killed the dinosaurs. Some think that other animals ate the dinosaurs' eggs. Then (2)_____ dinosaurs could not be born.

We know the weather changed at that time. One idea is that a meteor hit Earth. That made big clouds of dust. The dust blocked the sun for many years. It got very (3)_____. Ice covered everything. The dinosaurs could not survive.

No one really knows for sure what happened to the dinosaurs. What do you think?

Look back at the passage. Choose the correct word to fill in the blank.

1 A. water   C. ice
   B. meat   D. eggs

2 A. baby   C. swimming
   B. big   D. sick

3 A. hot   C. red
   B. wet   D. cold

CHARLAYNE HUNTER-GAULT

In 1961, a brave young girl went to college. The school was in Georgia. Charlayne Hunter-Gault (say shar•LANE HUN•ter•galt) was the first African American to go to (4)_____ there. At the time, things were very unfair for African Americans. There were places they could not go. They did not vote. They had separate schools. It was not a (5)_____ time in America.

Charlayne had to work very hard. Often, she was lonely. But she knew that she was doing something important. What she did helped change things in America.

Charlayne wanted to help people remember history. She worked for a newspaper. She did (6)_____ about poor neighborhoods. She helped make things better for many people.

Today, Charlayne is on a TV news show. Every night she helps people. She tells what is going on in the world.

Look back at the passage. Choose the correct word to fill in the blank.

4   A. work   C. college
    B. sea   D. Georgia

5   A. sad   C. ugly
    B. good   D. unfair

6   A. movies   C. songs
    B. schools   D. stories

LIGHTBULBS

How many people does it take to change a lightbulb? You could say it takes a lot of people! Most lightbulbs do not last long. Some last for a few months. Some only (7)_____ for a few weeks! Most lightbulbs have to be replaced many times.

Why do they stop working? It is because of the material inside. There are tiny wires (8)_____ the glass. They can break easily. Then you have to throw the bulb away.

There is one lightbulb that has never stopped working. It is in a fire station. The bulb has never been turned off. It is left on day and (9)_____. This lightbulb has been on for more than 75 years! Most lightbulbs are not that sturdy.

There are some new kinds of lightbulbs. One kind is made of stronger stuff. It does not (10)_____ so quickly. Now you can get lightbulbs that will last for two years. They cost more money. But it might be worth it if you don't like to change lightbulbs.

Look back at the passage. Choose the correct word to fill in the blank.

7   A. sing   C. walk
    B. work   D. light

8   A. inside   C. outside
    B. under   D. over

9   A. day   C. light
    B. night   D. bulb

10 A. light   C. break
    B. wish   D. bulb

Now use the Answer Key to check your answers. Mark the number you got correct on the Progress Chart.

LESSON 23

VOCABULARY

objects . . . things
sculptor . . someone who makes things out of clay

sculpture . . . an art piece that is made out of clay
legend . . . . . an old story

Read each passage. Then choose the correct word to fill in the blank.

MICHAEL NARANJO

Michael Naranjo (say na•RON•hoe) was in a war. He was fighting out in a field. A bomb dropped, and Michael was hurt. He lost his sight. And he could not use his right hand. Michael was in the hospital for a long time. One day, a nurse asked if he wanted anything. He said he wanted some clay.

First he made a worm with the (1)_____. Then he made a goldfish. Michael said, "I knew they looked okay because people could tell what they were." Soon Michael was (2)_____ all sorts of objects.

Michael went back to his home in New Mexico. He became a sculptor. He makes animals and people. He makes American Indian figures. He has become famous for his (3)_____.

One day, Michael went to a museum. He wanted to touch the sculptures. That was the only way he could (4)_____ them. At first, the museum people said he could put on gloves. Michael said no. He

had to feel the sculptures with his (5)_____. He said, "Wearing gloves is like asking sighted people to look at art with sunglasses on." Finally, he got to touch the sculptures.

When Michael shows his artwork, he always puts out a sign. It says, "Please Touch."

Look back at the passage. Choose the correct word to fill in the blank.

1 A. bomb   C. clay
   B. nurse   D. hurt

2 A. making   C. breaking
   B. swimming   D. winning

3 A. animals   C. wars
   B. sculptures   D. worms

4 A. see   C. break
   B. open   D. make

5 A. sculpture   C. fingers
   B. clay   D. eyes

THE MYSTERY OF BIGFOOT

In many parts of the world, there is a legend. It is about a strange creature. It looks a little like an ape. But it also looks human. It is tall and covered with hair. It walks on two (6)_____. Sometimes it makes a loud sound. It is very shy. It runs away when people come (7)_____.

Some call this creature Bigfoot. Some call it a Yeti. That means "Wild Man of the Mountains." Some early American Indians called it Sasquatch (say SAS-kwach). Many people have seen the creature, but no one has ever caught one. The Sasquatch (8)_____ away too fast.

One person took a movie of Bigfoot. Others have seen the big footprints. Scientists have studied the movie. They have looked at the footprints. They have listened to people's (9)_____. The Bigfoot is always described the same way. People have been telling stories about Bigfoot for many years.

Many believe that Bigfoot is not real. It is hard to know for sure. No one has ever seen one up close. But maybe that is okay. Would you want to get (10)_____ to a "Wild Man of the Mountain"?

Look back at the passage. Choose the correct word to fill in the blank.

6 A. wings   C. heads
   B. legs   D. tails

7 A. far   C. near
   B. behind   D. away

8 A. runs   C. walk
   B. fly   D. stand

9 A. songs   C. talk
   B. movies   D. stories

10 A. far   C. walk
   B. close   D. up

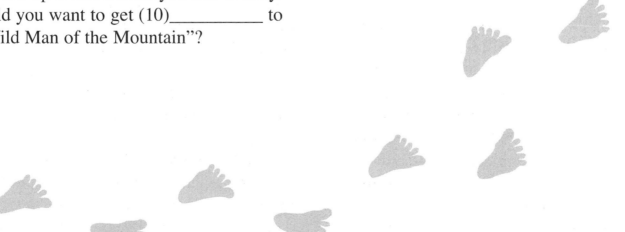

Now use the Answer Key to check your answers. Mark the number you got correct on the Progress Chart.

LESSON 24

VOCABULARY

extinct . . . . . . not one left alive
danger . . . . . . in trouble
species . . . . . . a kind of creature

endangered . . . . something that is in trouble

Read this passage. It is about the biggest animal in the world. Then choose the correct answer for each question.

What is the biggest animal that ever lived? Did you guess the elephant? Or maybe the dinosaur? Both guesses would be wrong. The biggest animal ever is still alive on Earth today. It is the great blue whale.

An adult blue whale is 95 feet long. That is longer that two city buses. It weighs many tons. It needs to eat four tons of food each day. The whale opens its mouth. It takes a gulp of seawater. A whale can swallow 45 tons of (7)_____ at one time. Then it strains the water through its baleen. The baleens are like the whale's teeth.

The whale is a mammal. That means it has to have air. First it comes up to the (8)_____ of the water. It takes a big breath. Then it can swim underwater for more than 50 minutes. The blue whale can hold a lot of air in its lungs. When it finally comes up, it takes another big breath. Its nose is on top of its head. That helps the whale breathe better.

Blue whales can also "talk." They make a loud sound in the water. It is a moaning sound. Some people think it sounds like a song. The water carries the (9)_____. Other whales can hear it from far away. The whales seem to have special songs. Other whales can tell what they are saying.

Every year, blue whales travel from place to place. In summer, the whales head up north. They eat the tiny fish that grow in the cold water. In the winter, they swim south to warmer waters. Sometimes, people can watch the whales (10)_____ by.

The blue whale also has a lot of fat on its body. That helps it stay warm. It also helps the whale float in the water. Whale fat is called blubber. People used to hunt whales for their blubber. They would make oil with it. The whale was hunted a lot. Because of that, the blue whale almost became extinct.

Today, the blue whale is protected from hunting. Several have been spotted in the ocean. But this beautiful creature is still in danger. It would be terrible to lose the blue whale forever. That is why it is still an endangered species.

Identifying the Sequence

1 When the blue whale gets ready to dive, what does it do first?

   A. It plays in the water.
   B. It eats lots of food.
   C. It takes a deep breath.
   D. It goes up north.

2 What does the whale do next?

   A. It plays in the water.
   B. It dives deep in the water.
   C. It takes a deep breath.
   D. It eats a lot of food.

Identifying Details

3 The blue whale is—

   A. the biggest animal alive
   B. a big eater
   C. a very loud singer
   D. a very fast swimmer

4 People hunted the blue whale for—

   A. mammal
   B. fun
   C. water
   D. blubber

Understanding the Main Idea

5 What is the main idea?

   A. The blue whale can swim very far.
   B. The blue whale is a rare animal.
   C. The blue whale can sing underwater.
   D. The blue whale can eat a lot.

6 What is the best title?

   A. The Fish That Holds Its Breath
   B. How to Catch a Whale
   C. A Very Hungry Creature
   D. The Biggest Creature Ever

Using the Context

Look back at the passage. Choose the correct word to fill in the blank.

7 A. air   C. water
   B. baleen   D. mammals

8 A. top   C. bottom
   B. under   D. wave

9 A. whale   C. baleen
   B. sound   D. wave

10 A. flying   B. eating
    C. swimming   D. playing

Now use the Answer Key to check your answers. Mark the number you got correct on the Progress Chart.

UNIT 5
LESSON 25

Skill Focus: Drawing Conclusions

Sometimes you need to figure out things that are not told in a story. This is called Drawing Conclusions. A conclusion is what you can tell from what you read. Here are some clues to help you:

- Read the story carefully.
- Think about what the writer tells about in the story.
- Use clues to draw conclusions about what the writer did not tell in the story.
- Read the story again. Check your conclusion.

VOCABULARY

hustled . . . . . ran fast
magnifies . . . . makes hotter or bigger

energy . . . . . power to do something
confidence . . being sure of someone

Read each passage. Then choose the correct answer.

A GREY DAY

Meg was halfway down the sidewalk. Then she looked at the dark gray sky. She went back in the house. She put on her raincoat, boots, and hat. Meg opened her umbrella as she stepped outdoors.

1 You can tell that—

    A. Meg wanted to stay inside.
    B. Meg didn't want to get wet.
    C. It was a warm day.
    D. It was nighttime.

2 From the story you can tell that—

    A. Meg got wet.
    B. Meg didn't like her house.
    C. The sun was shining.
    D. It had started to rain.

THE EARLY BIRD

Skip got out of bed. Today was a big day. He and Scoop were going to the car show. Skip grabbed some breakfast. He hustled over to Scoop's house. He knocked on the door. Finally, Scoop opened the door. He looked sleepy. He said, "What are doing up at this hour, Skip?"

3 You can tell that—

A. Scoop was asleep when Skip knocked.
B. Scoop lived far away from Skip.
C. Skip did not like Scoop.
D. Skip did not have a good breakfast.

4 From the story you can tell that—

A. Scoop did not want to go to the show.
B. Skip did not get up early.
C. Scoop did not like Skip.
D. Skip got up too early for the show.

WATERING PLANTS

Don't water your plants when it is sunny. The water gets on the leaves. The water magnifies the sun's heat. The plant's leaves could burn. It is better to water plants when the sun is low in the sky.

5 You can tell that—

A. Plants don't need water.
B. The sun could burn a plant.
C. Plants do not grow in the sun.
D. Plants like the dark.

6 From the story you can tell that—

A. It is better not to grow plants at all.
B. It is better to have plants inside.
C. It is best to water plants early.
D. It is best to not water your plants.

THE SWIM MEET

Meg and Kate ran into the kitchen. "Coach made us swim a mile today," said Kate. "Swimming makes me hungry!"

"Sit down, girls," said Mom, "You need energy for the swim meet tomorrow. I have a lot of confidence in you two!"

7 You can tell that—

A. Meg and Kate will win the meet.
B. Mom will get the girls some food.
C. Mom did not want the girls to swim.
D. Kate does not like swimming.

8 From the story you can tell that—

A. Meg and Kate do not eat.
B. Mom is hungry.
C. Meg and Kate will win the meet.
D. Meg and Kate will swim tomorrow.

THE BEAR CUB

Scoop and Skip were hiking in a big park. Skip saw a baby bear. He wanted to play with it. "Don't play with that bear cub," said Scoop. "The mother bear is never very far away."

9 You can tell that—

A. It is fun to play with bears.
B. The park was too big.
C. The bears are wild.
D. The mother bear is nice.

10 From the story you can tell that—

A. The mother bear will be angry.
B. The baby bear will sleep.
C. Scoop and Skip are lost.
D. Scoop will play with the bears.

Now use the Answer Key to check your answers. Mark the number you got correct on the Progress Chart.

UNIT 5
LESSON 26

VOCABULARY

equipment . . something you use for work or play

inquired . . . asked

galloping . . . . the way some animals run

soothingly . . . in a calm way

Read each passage. Then choose the correct answer.

THE PLAYGROUND

There was a school in New York City. They needed new playground equipment. They had a few swings and a slide. But they needed something to climb on. One day, a teacher was walking by the fire station. The firefighters were getting rid of an old fire engine. The teacher inquired about it. She said, "I know a good place for that fire engine. The children will love it!"

The children got something new to climb. It was bright red, and it had a big bell. Soon it was everyone's favorite.

1 You can tell that—

A. The children did not like swings.
B. The firefighters did not need the fire engine.
C. The firefighters did not get a fire engine.
D. The school wanted a new fire engine.

2 From the story you can tell that—

A. They put more slides on the playground.

B. The firefighters built a playground.
C. They put the fire engine on the playground.
D. The children did not like swings.

FAST MOVERS

A turtle walks pretty slowly. Everyone knows that. It takes the turtle 10 hours to go one mile. Have you ever seen a snake move? They seem to go very fast. A snake can travel two miles in one hour. A house cat can really get around. It can travel 30 miles in one hour. The jackrabbit wins the race. The jackrabbit can run 45 miles in an hour!

3 You can tell that—

A. Snakes move slower than turtles.
B. Cats move faster than snakes.
C. Cats are as fast as rabbits.
D. Snakes are as fast as rabbits

4 From the story you can tell that—

A. Cats move the fastest.
B. Jackrabbits move slowly.
C. Jackrabbits move the fastest.
D. Snakes move the fastest.

THE PAPER

Meg had to write a paper. It was due on Tuesday. On Monday night, she said, "I have so much to do."

Meg went in her room. She sat down to write. Then she got up to sharpen her pencil. Then she watered her plants. She sat down again. In a minute she got up again. She went to the kitchen. She said she had to get some water.

Meg's mom said, "You will never get anything done this way, Meg!"

5 You can tell that—

A. Meg does not have any paper.
B. Meg does not like school.
C. Meg did not water her plants.
D. Meg did not want to write.

6 From the story you can tell that—

A. Meg put off writing the paper.
B. Meg did not know how to write.
C. Meg's mother would write the paper.
D. Meg would go to bed soon.

THE BIG RACE

Skip was out in front. He could hear the other horses galloping. "Come on, girl," he said to his horse, Shelly. "You can do it. I know you can!" Shelly shook her head. Skip patted her neck soothingly.

They came to the last jump. It looked so high! Would Shelly make it? There was no time to think. Up, up they went. Soon they crossed the finish line. The crowd cheered for Skip and Shelly!

7 You can tell that—

A. The other horses were close behind.
B. They were the only ones in the race.
C. Shelly did not like to race.
D. Skip did not trust his horse.

8 In the first paragraph, you can tell that—

A. Shelly did not like to race.
B. Shelly understood what Skip said.
C. Skip did not talk to Shelly.
D. Shelly was not running fast.

9 In the last paragraph, you can tell that—

A. Shelly did not make the jump.
B. Shelly did not like Skip.
C. The other horses made the jump.
D. Shelly and Skip made the jump.

10 In the story you can tell that—

A. Shelly did not like to race.
B. Shelly was an old horse.
C. Shelly and Skip won the race.
D. Another horse won the race.

Now use the Answer Key to check your answers. Mark the number you got correct on the Progress Chart.

LESSON 27

VOCABULARY

discriminate . . . tell the difference between two things
dissecting . . . . cutting apart

structure . . . . how something is made
organs . . . . . . the parts inside a body

Read each passage. Then choose the correct answer for each question.

NIGHT VISION

Most people work during the day. That is because we need the sun to see. Most of us can see in the dark, too. But we cannot see well. We can't see colors. We can't see the outlines of things. When the sun goes down, we get sleepy. We sleep until the sun comes up again.

Many creatures can see better at night. Their eyes have a different shape. The eye can take in more light. Animals like cats and wolves can hunt at night. They can't see colors in the dark. But they can discriminate shapes. That helps them find what they are looking for.

1 You can tell that—

A. Many people sleep too long at night.
B. Peoples' eyes are not made to see in the dark.
C. Many people can't see colors.
D. Many people sleep during the day.

2 You can tell that—

A. Cats sleep all day.
B. Cats can't sleep at night.

C. Cats can see in the dark.
D. Cats get too hot at night.

3 You can tell that—

A. Many animals can see better in the dark.
B. People who sleep at night could go hunting.
C. People should learn to see at night.
D. Cats can see better than most people.

FREE THE FROGS

Here is some good news. There is a computer program that shows a frog. You can cut the frog apart. You can see the muscles under the skin. You can see the frog's organs. It is just like dissecting a frog. But it is not a real frog.

Now teachers can use this program for their science lessons. Students can learn about the structure of a frog. But no frogs have to be killed! That's good news for students. It is also good news for frogs!

4 You can tell that—

  A. Science teachers like to kill frogs.
  B. Science is not good to study.
  C. It is not fun to study frogs.
  D. Students used to have to dissect live frogs.

5 You can tell that the computer program—

  A. Uses a real frog.
  B. Has a fake frog.
  C. Is not science.
  D. Is not fun to use.

6 You can tell that—

  A. Science teachers like frogs.
  B. You can't learn much from a computer.
  C. There are no more frogs left.
  D. It is better not to kill frogs.

MEG'S NEW BAG

Dave gave Meg a new bag. "What should I put in it?" asked Meg.

"You can put your gym clothes in it," said Dave. "It's just the right size."

"It's too nice for that," said Meg. "I want to use it for something special." Meg took the bag home. Jake the cat met her at the door.

"That's a nice, sturdy bag, Meg," said Mom. "What will you use it for?"

"I don't know what to do with it. It has these vents at the top. It is a nice size. Not too big and not too small. I know I could use it for something special."

"We'll have to decide about that later," said Mom. "We have to take Jake to the vet."

"That's it!" yelled Meg. "This will be a great pet carrier for Jake!"

7 You can tell that Meg—

  A. Liked the bag a lot.
  B. Did not like the bag.
  C. Did not like Dave.
  D. Did not have a cat.

8 You can tell that—

  A. Meg did not like gym class.
  B. Meg can't decide what to do with the bag.
  C. Dave did not want the bag.
  D. Meg did not want the new bag.

9 You can tell that—

  A. The bag was very small.
  B. The bag would make a good trash can.
  C. The bag would be good to carry a pet.
  D. The bag would probably fall apart.

10 You can tell that—

  A. Meg will use the bag to carry Jake.
  B. Meg never did use the bag.
  C. Meg gave the bag to her mom.
  D. Dave took the bag back.

Now use the Answer Key to check your answers. Mark the number you got correct on the Progress Chart.

LESSON 28

VOCABULARY

cells . . . . . . bits of living matter
surface . . . . the top of something
slimy . . . . . slick

vitamins . . . . . things that help the body work right
edible . . . . . . something you can eat

Read each passage. Then choose the correct answer for each question.

SKIN

Look at your skin. Does it seem nice and smooth? Guess again! Up close, it looks very different. It has lots of deep lines. There are bumps that look like mountains. Some say it looks like the surface of the moon!

Now look at your skin again. Do you think it never changes? Don't be fooled! Your skin changes all the time. Old cells fall off. You wash them off when you take a bath. New cells take their place. They say that we grow a whole new skin every few months.

Other creatures lose their skin. They grow out of the old skin. The toad chews the skin off. A snake's skin gets too tight. The snake wiggles out. It leaves a big piece of skin. Sometimes you find snakeskins on the ground.

1 You can tell that—

   A. Your skin is very old.
   B. Your skin never changes.
   C. Your skin is not nice.
   D. Your skin is not smooth.

2 You can tell that your skin—

   A. Is very, very old.
   B. Changes all the time.
   C. Is always the same.
   D. Is like snakeskin.

3 You can tell that a snake—

   A. Grows too big for its skin.
   B. Does not have much skin.
   C. Likes to chew on skin.
   D. Is like people's skin.

LET'S EAT

How about some weeds for lunch? Or some flowers and leaves for a snack? Don't be so surprised. We eat lettuce and spinach. They are both leaves. They have lots of vitamins.

People have often picked weeds for food. Dandelions are good in salads. There is another weed called pokeweed. It is very good for you. It also tastes good. People have cooked it with onions.

Have you ever had seaweed? Seaweed grows in the ocean. It is dark green. It is pretty slimy when it is wet. But it has a salty taste. People eat it with fish and rice.

Sometime you could eat flowers. Many flowers are edible. You can put them in salads. They make the salad pretty. They are also good to eat.

4 You can tell that—

A. Many people don't eat lettuce.
B. Weeds can be good for you.
C. All weeds are bad for you.
D. All weeds are pretty.

5 You can tell that many people—

A. Eat seaweed every day.
B. Don't like to eat healthy foods.
C. Don't think weeds are good food.
D. Eat flowers every day.

6 You can tell that most people—

A. Would not think of eating flowers.
B. Think of flowers as food.
C. Do not like flowers.
D. Like to eat flowers with fish and rice.

THE VACATION

Sarah was gloomy. She was going to spend her vacation with Aunt Deb. Aunt Deb lived in an apartment. There was no yard. There were no kids to play with. Aunt Deb didn't even have any video games. Sarah thought it would be a long week.

The first day, Aunt Deb said, "We're going someplace different today. It's a surprise."

"Will it be fun?" asked Sarah. "I don't want to go if it's boring."

"I think you will like it," said Aunt Deb. "It's something you've never done before." They got in the car. They drove to a dock. They got on a big boat. They headed out along the coast.

"I've been on a boat before," said Sarah. "There's nothing special about this!" But suddenly, something jumped out of the water. It was huge. It was a whale! The people jumped and clapped.

"Wow!" said Sarah, "I've never seen a whale up close! This is great !"

7 You can tell that—

A. Sarah had never been on a boat.
B. Sarah didn't think she would have fun.
C. Sarah didn't like Aunt Deb.
D. Sarah did not know how to swim.

8 You can that Sarah's aunt—

A. Lived in a house.
B. Didn't like children.
C. Didn't like big boats.
D. Wanted her to have fun.

9 You can tell that Sarah—

A. Was surprised to see the whale.
B. Had already seen a whale.
C. Wanted to get in a car.
D. Did not like to ride on boats.

10 You can tell that Sarah—

A. Wanted to get off the boat.
B. Wanted to live in an apartment.
C. Was enjoying her vacation.
D. Wanted to go home.

Now use the Answer Key to check your answers. Mark the number you got correct on the Progress Chart.

LESSON 29

VOCABULARY

impressed . . . to think something is very good

unearthed . . dug up

calendar . . . something that keeps the days in order

ruins . . . . . buildings left behind

Read each passage. Then choose the correct answer for each question.

PHILLIS WHEATLEY

In 1753, Phillis Wheatley came to America. She was from Africa. She was only eight years old. She did not come because she wanted to. Phillis was a slave. She had been taken away from her family. She rode on a slave ship to America. At the time, many Americans had slaves. They did not understand how wrong this was.

Phillis was sick and scared the day she was sold. But in some ways she was lucky. The people who bought her were kind. They wanted a little girl to help in the house. Phillis did not have a hard job.

The family was named Wheatley. They gave Phillis that name, too. They had a little girl named Mary. Mary knew how to read. She helped Phillis learn to read, too. Phillis read everything she could find. She also learned how to write. Phillis could write very well. She started to write poems.

Phillis wrote poems about her life. She told about going away from her home. She told about the sadness of being a slave. Mr. Wheatley read some of her poems. He was impressed with Phillis's writing. He showed them to other people. Phillis became known as the "slave poet." Her poems were read all over the world.

The Wheatleys gave Phillis her freedom. She got married and had children. Phillis died when she was only 30 years old. But her poems had shown people that slaves were human beings. She taught white Americans an important lesson.

1 You can tell that Phillis—

    A. Liked to ride boats.
    B. Was forced to go to America.
    C. Did not like her new family.
    D. Was glad to get to leave Africa.

2 You can tell that—

    A. The Wheatleys lived in Africa.
    B. The Wheatleys were not nice.
    C. The Wheatleys did not like slaves.
    D. The Wheatleys were good to Phillis.

3 You can tell that Phillis—

    A. Never learned to read.
    B. Didn't like to read.
    C. Was very bright.
    D. Didn't work hard.

4 From the story you can tell that—

    A. Most slaves were not taught to read.
    B. Most slaves did not want to learn.
    C. All slaves went to school.
    D. Most slaves were free.

5 From the story you can tell that—

    A. Phillis had a happy life.
    B. Phillis had a hard life.
    C. Phillis went back to Africa.
    D. Phillis didn't like the Wheatleys.

A MYSTERIOUS CITY

Scientists were exploring in Mexico. They were digging in the jungle. Someone found some stones in the ground. Soon they realized they had found a building. They were very excited! But it got better. There was more than one building. The scientists had found a lost city!

The city was named Chichen Itza (say CHEE•chen EET•sa). The Mayan people lived there long ago. They could write. They also understood math. They invented a calendar. The Maya had ruled all of Mexico. They had many beautiful cities. But Chichen Itza was the greatest city of all.

The scientists unearthed the city. They started to study the ruins. Chichen Itza is built out of stone. Each block of stone was fitted together. How did people move the heavy stones? No one knows for sure.

The city had a sports arena. It is a lot like the arenas we have today. This one is called the Ball Court. You can stand at one end of the Ball Court and whisper. A person on the other end can hear you! How did they do that?

There are many more mysteries at Chichen Itza. We may never know the answers to them all.

6 You can tell that—

    A. The city was easy to find.
    B. The city was buried in the ground.
    C. The city was not very interesting.
    D. People still live in the city.

7 You can tell that—

    A. It was easy to build the city.
    B. The city was made of wood.
    C. The city was small.
    D. It was hard to build the city.

8 You can tell that the Maya—

    A. Were very poor people.
    B. Did not know how to read.
    C. Had made many discoveries.
    D. Did not take care of the city.

9 You can tell that the sports arena—

    A. Was made by someone very smart.
    B. Was made by accident.
    C. Was not a good place to play.
    D. Was very small.

10 You can tell from the story that—

    A. We can't learn much from the Maya.
    B. The city is too far away to visit.
    C. We can learn a lot from the Maya.
    D. The Maya were foolish people.

Now use the Answer Key to check your answers. Mark the number you got correct on the Progress Chart.

LESSON 30

VOCABULARY

surrounded . . things all around you

conditions . . . different types of weather

unique . . . . . not like anything else

treasure . . . something that is worth a lot

created . . . . made

creation . . . something that is made

Read the passage. It is about Luther Burbank. Then choose the correct answer for each question.

LUTHER BURBANK

Luther Burbank was born in 1849. He grew up on a farm. Luther liked to observe plants. He noticed that some did well in the hot sun. Some did better in the shade. That gave Luther an idea.

Luther made a greenhouse. He would try growing all kinds of plants. He would watch how they did in different conditions. Luther tried putting the seeds of two different plants together. They would make a unique new plant.

Luther experimented with many plants. He came up with a new kind of potato. It would not rot in the ground. That was a problem with most other potatoes. They called it the Luther Potato. Today it is called the Idaho Russet.

Luther sold his potato plant for $150. Luther knew this was his chance to start a new life. He and his brothers set out for California. There were many other people coming to California to find gold. But Luther was not interested in gold. He looked around the beautiful state. He knew

that he had found a treasure that was better than gold.

Luther moved to a small town in California. It was called Santa Rosa. The weather there was very mild. It never got too hot or too cold. It was the perfect place to grow things. Luther bought some land. He built a greenhouse. He started his (7)_____ experiments again. For awhile, Luther lived in an old chicken coop. He didn't build a house until later. But he didn't care. What mattered most to him were his plants.

Luther wanted to make new kinds of plants. He wanted them to be stronger and grow better. That way, there could be more food for people all over the world.

For the next 50 years, Luther Burbank created new plants. He created over 800 new kinds of plants. Many of these were fruit trees, nut trees, and grains. He also created hundreds of new flowers. Luther became famous for his work. Today we see Luther's (8)_____ and vegetables every day. Look at a potato, a plum, or a grape. It may be a Luther Burbank creation.

Identifying the Sequence

1 What did Luther Burbank do first?

A. He mined for gold.
B. He made a new potato.
C. He went to Calfornia.
D. He made new trees.

2 What did he do last?

A. He grew up on a farm.
B. He made a new potato.
C. He mined for gold.
D. He moved to Santa Rosa.

Identifying Details

3 Luther Burbank created—

A. a gold mine
B. California
C. a new potato
D. all vegetables

4 Luther lived—

A. in a chicken coop
B. in a greenhouse
C. in a gold mine
D. on a boat

Understanding the Main Idea

5 What is the main idea?

A. Luther Burbank did not go far from home.
B. Luther Burbank went to California to get rich.
C. Luther Burbank was not very interested in people.
D. Luther Burbank helped make food better for people.

6 What is the best title?

A. The Plant Maker
B. An American Leader
C. A Lazy Man
D. A Gold Miner

Using the Context

Look back at the passage. Choose the correct word to fill in the blank.

7 A. gold   C. book
     B. plant   D. farm

8 A. California   C. fruits
     B. rocks   D. gold

Drawing Conclusions

9 You can tell that Luther—

A. Wanted to make things better for people.
B. Wanted to get rich in Calfornia.
C. Wanted to become a famous person.
D. Did not like to travel.

10 You can tell that Luther—

A. Liked to live in cold weather.
B. Tried many plant experiments.
C. Got tired of working with plants.
D. Got rich at gold mining.

Now use the Answer Key to check your answers. Mark the number you got correct on the Progress Chart.

LESSON 31

Skill Focus: Making Inferences

Sometimes a writer does not tell you everything in a story. You have to use clues from the story to answer some questions. This is called making inferences. Inference is a guess you make about the story. Here are some clues to help you:

- Read the story carefully.
- Look for clues to help you get ideas about what the writer did not say.
- Think about things that you have seen and done. Use what you know to make an inference.
- Think about the writer's opinion. This will help you make an inference.
- Reread the story. Look for things that support your inference.

VOCABULARY

thrilled . . . very happy
excellent . . very good

canyon . . . . a very deep valley

Read each passage. Then choose the correct answer for each question.

A NEW FRIEND

Scoop and Skip went to an animal shelter. "I am going to get a cat," said Skip. "I'll give it to my little sister. She'll love it."

"That's great," said Scoop. "But I need to get a buddy for Ruff. I am going to look for a friendly puppy."

1 Which is probably true?

　A. Skip does have a pet.
　B. Scoop already has a dog.
　C. Skip does not like cats.
　D. The cats like the shelter.

2 Which is probably true?

　A. Skip is a cat.
　B. Ruff is a cat.
　C. Ruff is a dog.
　D. Scoop is a dog.

A GOOD JOB

"I wish I could get a new snowboard," said Jim. "But first I'll have to get a job." Jim went up and down his street. He asked his neighbors if they needed any chores done. He got lots of work. Soon Jim had his new snowboard.

3 Which is probably true?

    A. Jim had no friends.
    B. Jim needed money.
    C. Jim wants to surf.
    D. Jim did not like to work.

4 Which is probably true?

    A. Jim did a lot of chores.
    B. Jim did not get a snowboard.
    C. Jim did not like to work.
    D. Jim did not do the chores.

THE E-MAIL

Meg bought her first computer. She was thrilled. She set it up. Then she sat down to work. She went to her e-mail. There was a message! The message said, "Hi, friend! Glad to have you on e-mail. Your pal, Jan."

5 Which is probably true?

    A. Jan bought her computer.
    B. Meg didn't like computers.
    C. Jan does not have a computer.
    D. Meg was happy to have a computer.

6 Which is probably true?

    A. Jan knew Meg's e-mail address.
    B. Jan sent Meg a postcard.
    C. Meg and Jan are not friends.
    D. Meg broke the computer.

DINNERTIME

Skip and his mom came in the house. They took their bags to the kitchen. Skip got out some chicken and noodles. His mom took out some vegetables and bread. Then she got out her soup pot. They made an excellent dinner.

7 Which is probably true about Skip and his mom?

    A. They came from the car shop.
    B. They came from a restaurant.
    C. Skip was going to make breakfast.
    D. They came from the grocery store.

8 Which is probably true?

    A. Skip's mom went upstairs.
    B. Skip went to bed.
    C. Skip and his mom made soup.
    D. Skip doesn't like to cook.

A LONG DAY

Jake went on a hike. It was a nice day. He walked a long way up the canyon. Three hours later Jake looked up. The sun was going down. He ran home for dinner. No one was in the kitchen. There was a plate with a note on it.

9 Which is probably true?

    A. Jake fell asleep.
    B. Jake forgot dinner.
    C. Jake hiked too far.
    D. Jake got lost.

10 Which is probably true?

    A. Jake ate on the hike.
    B. Jake was late for dinner.
    C. Jake was not hungry.
    D. Jake went to bed.

Now use the Answer Key to check your answers. Mark the number you got correct on the Progress Chart.

UNIT 6
LESSON 32

VOCABULARY

serious . . . . . dangerous
volunteer . . . . do a job for free

survive . . . . . to live through something
adapted . . . . . to get used to something

Read each passage. Then choose the correct answer for each question.

A HOSPITAL HELPER

Mr. Jordan was 65 years old. He did not work anymore. But he needed something to do. Mr. Jordan missed being around people.

One day, Mr. Jordan went to visit a friend in the hospital. She had a serious operation. She would have to be in the hospital for awhile. Mr. Jordan came to visit her every day.

Soon, Mr. Jordan noticed other patients. He saw that they didn't have visitors. Now Mr. Jordan volunteers at the hospital. He visits the patients. He reads to them. Or they just talk. Mr. Jordan helps people feel better.

1 Which is probably true?

A. Mr. Jordan doesn't like people.
B. Mr. Jordan likes to help out.
C. Mr. Jordan was sick.
D. Mr. Jordan likes hospitals.

2 Which is probably true?

A. Visiting patients helps Mr. Jordan feel good.
B. The hospital is close to Mr. Jordan's house.

C. The patients don't like visiting with Mr. Jordan.
D. Mr Jordan works at the hospital.

THE SLIDING HIGHWAY

There is a strange place in California. It is right by the ocean. There are many steep cliffs. The hills are made of soft dirt. Every year, parts of the hills fall into the ocean.

There is a road on the cliffs. People like to drive on it. But it is very narrow. When the hills slide, the road slides, too. The road is always sliding into the ocean! This does not sound very safe. Some people want to move the road somewhere else. But others love to drive the road. It is a beautiful view.

3 Which is probably true about the road?

A. It is a very big road.
B. People don't like to go there.
C. It is a very dangerous place.
D. It is easy to drive on.

4 Which is probably true?

A. They should move the road.
B. The road can be made wider.

C. The hills will stop sliding.
D. People will stop driving on the road.

POLAR BEARS

Polar bears live in the North Pole. It is a very cold place. There is ice and snow everywhere. There are no trees or bushes. How does the polar bear survive such harsh weather?

The polar bear has beautiful white fur. There is long fur at the bottom of its feet. It protects the feet from the cold. The fur is very stiff on the bear's legs. That helps the bear swim. Polar bears swim to catch their food. They have adapted well to the cold weather.

5 Which is probably true about the North Pole?

A. It is easy to live there.
B. People drive cars there.
C. It is not a good place for polar bears.
D. It is hard to find food there.

6 Which is probably true about polar bears?

A. They like to swim.
B. Their fur is not warm.
C. They don't like fish.
D. They don't like the cold.

7 Which is probably true?

A. Polar bears like warm weather.
B. Polar bears like cold weather.
C. Polar bears don't like ice.
D. Polar bears cannot swim.

THE PIZZA

Meg was having a party. She wanted to make pizza. Her little sister Liz was going to help. Meg made the dough. She flattened it on the pizza pan. Then she went to clean her room.

Liz came in to the kitchen. She saw the dough in the pan. She decided to finish the pizza herself. She would surprise Meg. She put all her favorite things on the pizza. She put in some chocolate. Then she added some grapes. She put some strawberry jam on top. Then she put it in the oven. Meg was surprised when Liz pulled out the pizza!

8 Which is probably true?

A. Meg does not know how to cook.
B. Liz was trying to mess up Meg's pizza.
C. Meg has never had pizza.
D. Liz did not know how to make pizza.

9 Which is probably true?

A. Meg put things she liked on the pizza.
B. Liz put things she liked on the pizza.
C. Meg likes to make pizza.
D. Liz and Meg don't like each other.

10 Which is probably true?

A. No one came to the party.
B. Everyone loved the pizza.
C. Meg made another pizza.
D. Liz did not have any friends.

Now use the Answer Key to check your answers. Mark the number you got correct on the Progress Chart.

LESSON 33

VOCABULARY

alphabet . . . . . letters used to make words

relaxed . . . . . not tight

flexible . . . . . can move around easily

function . . . . . to work properly

Read each passage. Then choose the correct answer for each question.

THE CHEROKEE ALPHABET

The Cherokee people were like many other American Indian tribes. They did not write things down. They did not have an alphabet. They could not write the history of their people. One man changed all that. His name was Sequoyah (say se•KWOY•a).

Sequoyah was a Cherokee leader. He met with many white leaders. He wanted to protect his people's rights. He saw the white people writing their ideas on paper. He saw that this was a powerful tool.

Sequoyah decided to make an alphabet for the Cherokee language. Then his people could write things down. They could pass on their culture. Soon, there were Cherokee newspapers and books. The books had old Cherokee stories. Now people could read about Cherokee history. They could keep their culture alive. Sequoyah gave his people a great gift.

1 Which is probably true?

  A. Sequoyah did not learn to read.
  B. Sequoyah wanted to write a book.
  C. Sequoyah was a greedy man.
  D. Sequoyah cared about his people.

2 Which is probably true about the Cherokee people?

  A. They did not like the alphabet.
  B. They liked having an alphabet.
  C. They did not read any books.
  D. They did not care about books.

3 Which is probably true?

  A. Sequoyah knew that it was important to write.
  B. Sequoyah wanted to be like the white leaders.
  C. The Cherokee people lived a long time ago.
  D. The Cherokee people do not know history.

YOUR SPINE

Do you know how tall you are? Sometimes you are even taller. Everyone is a little taller in the morning. When you get up your body is relaxed. Your spine can stretch out.

Your spine is very strong. But it is also flexible. You can stand up straight. But you can also twist around. The human body could not function without the spine.

It is important to take care of your spine. It can get too stiff. You can pull a muscle. If your back hurts, it is hard to do anything. It is hard to sit or walk or run. It is not much fun to hurt your back.

4 Which is probably true?

A. You get taller every day.
B. You get shorter in the afternoon.
C. You get taller in the afternoon.
D. You get shorter every day.

5 Which is probably true?

A. Your spine is important.
B. Your spine is not very important.
C. Your spine can break in two.
D. Your spine is stiff.

6 Which is probably true when your spine hurts?

A. You can dance.
B. You can jump.
C. You have to lie down.
D. You do not hurt.

THE WALKERS CLUB

Mrs. Drake was almost 70 years old. Her doctor said she needed to get exercise. She decided to walk every day. Early one morning, she headed down the street. She saw her neighbor, Mrs. Lopez. "What are you doing out so early?" asked Mrs. Drake.

"I like to get out and walk before the kids get up," said Mrs. Lopez. The two neighbors agreed to walk together. It would be more fun that way.

The next day, the women were walking and ran into Mr. Lee. He was walking his dog. Mr. Lee said he was going to join a dogwalkers group. He invited the women to come. Every day, a large group of walkers get together. They call themselves The Walkers Club.

7 Which is probably true?

A. Mrs. Drake liked to walk with people.
B. Mrs. Drake didn't like to walk.
C. Mrs. Drake didn't get up early.
D. Mrs. Drake didn't like people.

8 Which is probably true?

A. Mrs. Lopez didn't like people.
B. Mrs. Lopez liked walking early.
C. Mrs. Lopez did not have kids.
D. Mrs. Lopez did not walk fast.

9 Which is probably true?

A. The two women enjoyed walking together.
B. Mrs. Lopez walked too fast.
C. Mrs. Drake walked too slow.
D. The neighbors walked at night.

10 Which is probably true?

A. Some people didn't like walking with dogs.
B. The Walkers Club was too big.
C. The Walkers Club was small.
D. The Walkers Club got new members.

Now use the Answer Key to check your answers. Mark the number you got correct on the Progress Chart.

LESSON 34

VOCABULARY

communicate . . let someone know what you think

gesture . . . . . . moving the hands

rescued . . . . . saved from harm

treasure . . . . . something of value

dismayed . . . . upset

Read each passage. Then choose the correct answer for each question.

TALKING BABIES

When did you learn to talk? Were you a year old? Were you even older? It often takes babies a long time to learn how to communicate with words.

Today, some babies go to an unusual class. They take the class with their parents. The teacher says a word. At the same time, she makes a gesture. She might say the word 'hungry.' Then she will move her hand in front of her face. Then the group has something to eat. The babies learn to use that same hand movement when they hear the word.

Some say this gives babies a way to communicate. If a baby is hungry, he can move his hands in front of his mouth. Then his mom knows what is wrong. It seems to work with some babies. But we still don't know everything a baby thinks.

1 Which is probably true?

   A. Most babies can't talk.
   B. It is easy for babies to learn to talk.
   C. Most babies do not get hungry.
   D. Most babies can feed themselves.

2 Which is probably true?

   A. Most babies do not learn to talk.
   B. Most babies do not want to learn things.
   C. Lots of babies learn how to sing songs.
   D. Some babies can learn hand movements.

3 Which is probably true?

   A. Hand movements help babies talk without words.
   B. Babies should not learn how to talk.
   C. Parents should not teach their babies.
   D. Babies should learn how to make their own food.

THE RESCUE

Jenny and Luke went for a walk. They walked by the lake. Suddenly, Luke started to bark. "Come on, Luke," said Jenny, "There's nothing out there." But Luke kept barking. Jenny pulled on the leash. She got Luke away from the lake.

They went to a field. They were going

to play frisbee. Jenny took off Luke's leash. Then he ran. Jenny ran after him.

There was a little sound coming from the lake. Jenny looked hard. Way out on the lake, she saw a boat. It had turned over! Someone was waving! Jenny ran quickly for help. The park ranger rescued the man.

Sometimes dogs bark at nothing. But this time, Luke's barking helped save someone's life.

4 Which is probably true?

A. Luke liked to bark at lakes.
B. Luke knew something was wrong.
C. Luke was not a nice dog.
D. Luke was lost.

5 Luke probably ran—

A. Back to the lake.
B. After the frisbee.
C. To his house.
D. After a car.

6 Which is probably true?

A. They let the person swim back.
B. Luke never came back to the park.
C. Luke liked to swim in the lake.
D. They got the person out of the lake.

COUSIN RAY

Jan and Lisa were excited. Cousin Ray was visiting. The kids sat out on the back porch.

"I bet there is treasure buried in the yard. We should dig for it." said Cousin Ray.

The kids started digging in the corner of the yard. They found some worms. They found some bottle caps. But no treasure.

Before they were done, there were holes all over the yard. They found an old sock and some bones the dog buried. They also found an old key. But they didn't find any treasure.

Mom was dismayed when she looked around the yard. Then she picked up the key. "I have been looking for this for over a year! It is the key to grandma's old chest. Thank you for finding this, kids!"

The girls looked over at Cousin Ray. He winked at them. "I'm glad we could help," he said with a big smile.

7 Which is probably true?

A. Cousin Ray didn't like to have fun.
B. Cousin Ray was not nice.
C. Cousin Ray liked adventures.
D. Cousin Ray did not come over.

8 Which is probably true?

A. There was treasure inside the house.
B. There wasn't treasure in the yard.
C. Cousin Ray had buried a treasure.
D. Cousin Ray planted a garden.

9 Which is probably true about Cousin Ray?

A. He had a lot of ideas.
B. He never had any ideas.
C. He was a mean kid.
D. He liked to dig gardens.

10 Which is probably true?

A. Cousin Ray never came over again.
B. Mom was mad at the kids.
C. Mom was glad to find her key.
D. Mom did not like Cousin Ray.

Now use the Answer Key to check your answers. Mark the number you got correct on the Progress Chart.

LESSON 35

VOCABULARY

chemicals . . . . . substances made to kill bugs

sharecroppers . . people who work on someone else's farm

investigation . . . . finding something out

segregated . . . . . . when people are kept apart from each other

Read each passage. Then choose the correct answer for each question.

RACHEL CARSON

When Rachel Carson was little, her mother took her on hikes. They would look at the birds and the trees. They would study the flowers.

When Rachel grew up, she wanted to help protect nature. She liked to write. She wrote reports for her job. She also wrote two books about the ocean. She told how important it was to protect the ocean.

One spring, Rachel was working in her garden. She noticed that were not many birds singing. She wanted to find out why. She did an investigation. She found out that chemicals were killing the birds. Fish and animals were dying, too. The chemicals were being sprayed on crops to kill bugs. But they were doing more than that.

Rachel wrote a book about chemical spraying. She called it *Silent Spring*. She said that chemicals were bad for animals and people. At the time, some people said she was wrong. Now we know that she was right. Many chemicals were banned. Rachel Carson helped the world be a safer place.

1 Which is probably true?

 A. Rachel Carson liked chemicals.
 B. Rachel Carson loved nature.
 C. Rachel Carson did not like bugs.
 D. Rachel Carson only read books.

2 Which was probably true?

 A. Rachel used her writing to tell people about nature.
 B. Rachel wanted to make a lot of money from her books.
 C. Rachel wanted to make movies.
 D. Rachel didn't care about animals.

3 Rachel probably—

 A. Wanted to be famous.
 B. Wanted to make things better.
 C. Wanted to work in her garden.
 D. Was very shy.

4 Which is probably true?

 A. People want to use more chemicals.
 B. People didn't care about birds.
 C. People didn't know about chemicals.
 D. People did not like Rachel's books.

5 Which is probably true?

    A. All chemicals are bad for you.
    B. Some chemicals are bad for people.
    C. We should use more chemicals in our gardens.
    D. We should use chemicals in our food.

JACKIE ROBINSON

Jackie Robinson was born in Georgia. His family were African-American share-croppers. They were very poor. Jackie was always a good athlete. He got to go to college. He played many sports there.

Jackie went into the army. At the time, the army was segregated. African-Americans were kept separate. One day, Jackie got on a bus. He refused to sit in the back seat. That got him in trouble. But Jackie knew it was the right thing to do.

Jackie became a very good baseball player. But the baseball teams were also segregated. Jackie and his team did not get paid well. People said they were not as good as the white teams. But Jackie was probably the best baseball player of his time.

Finally, a white team decided to hire Jackie. A lot of people did not like that. They yelled at Jackie when he played. But Jackie just ignored the people who didn't like him. He played the best baseball he could. He won a lot of games for his team.

Soon, other African-Americans were playing on white teams. Jackie's courage changed baseball forever.

6 Which is probably true?

    A. Jackie knew how to work hard.
    B. Jackie didn't care if he played baseball.
    C. Jackie didn't go in the army.
    D. Jackie played basketball for a living.

7 Which is probably true?

    A. Jackie didn't want to upset anyone.
    B. Jackie did not like most people.
    C. Jackie was very shy.
    D. Jackie believed that he should be treated fairly.

8 Some people probably believed—

    A. That African-Americans could not play baseball.
    B. That baseball was not a fair sport.
    C. That white players were better than African-Americans.
    D. That all sports teams should be stopped.

9 Which is probably true?

    A. People came to see Jackie play baseball.
    B. People didn't come to see Jackie play.
    C. People liked basketball more.
    D. Baseball was not a popular sport.

10 Which is probably true?

    A. Jackie was the best baseball player.
    B. Jackie made things worse for African-Americans.
    C. No one remembers Jackie.
    D. Jackie helped make things better for African-Americans.

Now use the Answer Key to check your answers. Mark the number you got correct on the Progress Chart.

LESSON 36

VOCABULARY

habitat ..... a place where animals live	**avalanche** ... when a lot of snow slides down a mountain
difficult .... very hard to do	
possessions .. things you own	**goldseekers** .. people who look for gold

Read the passage. It is about the gold rush in Alaska. Then choose the correct answer for each question.

Alaska is a beautiful place. Many people go there to see the mountains and icebergs. They can watch whales and polar bears in their natural habitat. But 100 years ago, people came to Alaska for a different reason.

Someone was digging in a creek. The creek was called Dawson's Creek. They looked down and saw something sparkling. There were pieces of gold lying on the sand! The word got out. Everyone could get rich! Soon there was a gold rush. People were coming to Alaska to dig for gold. They came from all over the world.

People ran into many problems along the way. It was very difficult to get to Dawson's Creek. The creek was really in Canada. But you had to go through Alaska to get there. The first obstacle was a big hill. It was called Chilcoot Hill. It was the only way to get over the mountains. It was very steep. People had to drag their possessions up the hill. Most people had to go up and down the hill five times. They had to take a lot of supplies for their trip. It was a dangerous climb. People had to climb up a narrow trail. If you slid, you could (6)_____ off the mountain. Many people died that way. There were also avalanches on Chilcoot Hill. One avalanche killed 100 people.

Once you got over the hill, you came to a lake. It was a very big lake. In the winter it was frozen. In summer the water went very fast. Some people tried to cross the ice. They thought that would be easier. Many people fell through the ice. They drowned in the cold water. Other people waited until spring. They built boats. Then they (7)_____ the boats across the lake. There were four more lakes after that. People had to sail over 500 miles to get to Dawson's Creek.

Finally, the luckiest people got to Dawson's Creek. But the hardest part was still ahead. It took over a year for most people to get there. By the time they got there, much of the gold was gone. People would work hard in the mines. But often they did not find gold. Most goldseekers did not come back rich. The gold rush did not live up to its promise.

Identifying the Sequence

1 What happened first?

A. People had to dig for gold
B. People had to climb a mountain
C. People had to build a boat
D. People lost everything

2 What happened last?

A. People had to dig for gold
B. People had to climb a mountain
C. People came to Alaska
D. People had to build a boat

Identifying Details

3 Chilcoot Pass was—

A. ice
B. wet
C. steep
D. soft

Understanding the Main Idea

4 What is the main idea?

A. Alaska is a dangerous place.
B. The Gold Rush did not live up to its promise.
C. The Gold Rush was not a real thing.
D. Everyone got rich in Alaska.

5 What is the best title?

A. The Steep Mountain
B. Alaska
C. Digging for Gold
D. The Gold Rush

Using the Context

Look back at the passage. Choose the correct word to fill in the blank.

6 A. fly   C. fall
B. jump   D. ride

7 A. sailed   C. swam
B. walk   D. carry

Drawing Conclusions

8 You can tell that—

A. People had a good time in Alaska.
B. People wanted to move to Alaska.
C. People wanted to make money in Alaska.
D. Alaska is an easy place to travel.

9 You can tell that—

A. Alaska did not have any gold.
B. A lot of people got rich in Alaska.
C. The people didn't care about gold.
D. A lot of people died along the way.

Making Inferences

10 Which is probably true?

A. People found out that looking for gold was hard work.
B. People saw that Alaska was an ugly place.
C. Everyone found gold.
D. People had a lot of fun getting to Dawson's Creek.

Now use the Answer Key to check your answers. Mark the number you got correct on the Progress Chart.

ANSWER SHEET

Name _____

Unit # _____ Skill _____

Lesson # _____

1. Ⓐ Ⓑ Ⓒ Ⓓ
2. Ⓐ Ⓑ Ⓒ Ⓓ
3. Ⓐ Ⓑ Ⓒ Ⓓ
4. Ⓐ Ⓑ Ⓒ Ⓓ
5. Ⓐ Ⓑ Ⓒ Ⓓ
6. Ⓐ Ⓑ Ⓒ Ⓓ
7. Ⓐ Ⓑ Ⓒ Ⓓ
8. Ⓐ Ⓑ Ⓒ Ⓓ
9. Ⓐ Ⓑ Ⓒ Ⓓ
10. Ⓐ Ⓑ Ⓒ Ⓓ

Lesson # _____

1. Ⓐ Ⓑ Ⓒ Ⓓ
2. Ⓐ Ⓑ Ⓒ Ⓓ
3. Ⓐ Ⓑ Ⓒ Ⓓ
4. Ⓐ Ⓑ Ⓒ Ⓓ
5. Ⓐ Ⓑ Ⓒ Ⓓ
6. Ⓐ Ⓑ Ⓒ Ⓓ
7. Ⓐ Ⓑ Ⓒ Ⓓ
8. Ⓐ Ⓑ Ⓒ Ⓓ
9. Ⓐ Ⓑ Ⓒ Ⓓ
10. Ⓐ Ⓑ Ⓒ Ⓓ

Lesson # _____

1. Ⓐ Ⓑ Ⓒ Ⓓ
2. Ⓐ Ⓑ Ⓒ Ⓓ
3. Ⓐ Ⓑ Ⓒ Ⓓ
4. Ⓐ Ⓑ Ⓒ Ⓓ
5. Ⓐ Ⓑ Ⓒ Ⓓ
6. Ⓐ Ⓑ Ⓒ Ⓓ
7. Ⓐ Ⓑ Ⓒ Ⓓ
8. Ⓐ Ⓑ Ⓒ Ⓓ
9. Ⓐ Ⓑ Ⓒ Ⓓ
10. Ⓐ Ⓑ Ⓒ Ⓓ

Lesson # _____

1. Ⓐ Ⓑ Ⓒ Ⓓ
2. Ⓐ Ⓑ Ⓒ Ⓓ
3. Ⓐ Ⓑ Ⓒ Ⓓ
4. Ⓐ Ⓑ Ⓒ Ⓓ
5. Ⓐ Ⓑ Ⓒ Ⓓ
6. Ⓐ Ⓑ Ⓒ Ⓓ
7. Ⓐ Ⓑ Ⓒ Ⓓ
8. Ⓐ Ⓑ Ⓒ Ⓓ
9. Ⓐ Ⓑ Ⓒ Ⓓ
10. Ⓐ Ⓑ Ⓒ Ⓓ

Lesson # _____

1. Ⓐ Ⓑ Ⓒ Ⓓ
2. Ⓐ Ⓑ Ⓒ Ⓓ
3. Ⓐ Ⓑ Ⓒ Ⓓ
4. Ⓐ Ⓑ Ⓒ Ⓓ
5. Ⓐ Ⓑ Ⓒ Ⓓ
6. Ⓐ Ⓑ Ⓒ Ⓓ
7. Ⓐ Ⓑ Ⓒ Ⓓ
8. Ⓐ Ⓑ Ⓒ Ⓓ
9. Ⓐ Ⓑ Ⓒ Ⓓ
10. Ⓐ Ⓑ Ⓒ Ⓓ

Lesson # _____

1. Ⓐ Ⓑ Ⓒ Ⓓ
2. Ⓐ Ⓑ Ⓒ Ⓓ
3. Ⓐ Ⓑ Ⓒ Ⓓ
4. Ⓐ Ⓑ Ⓒ Ⓓ
5. Ⓐ Ⓑ Ⓒ Ⓓ
6. Ⓐ Ⓑ Ⓒ Ⓓ
7. Ⓐ Ⓑ Ⓒ Ⓓ
8. Ⓐ Ⓑ Ⓒ Ⓓ
9. Ⓐ Ⓑ Ⓒ Ⓓ
10. Ⓐ Ⓑ Ⓒ Ⓓ

PROGRESS CHART

Lesson #	0	1	2	3	4	5	6	7	8	9	10
Lesson #	0	1	2	3	4	5	6	7	8	9	10
Lesson #	0	1	2	3	4	5	6	7	8	9	10
Lesson #	0	1	2	3	4	5	6	7	8	9	10
Lesson #	0	1	2	3	4	5	6	7	8	9	10
Lesson #	0	1	2	3	4	5	6	7	8	9	10
Review Lesson #	0	1	2	3	4	5	6	7	8	9	10

ANSWER KEY

UNIT 1—IDENTIFYING THE SEQUENCE

Unit 1 Lesson 1	Unit 1 Lesson 2	Unit 1 Lesson 3
1. B	1. C	1. B
2. C	2. A	2. D
3. B	3. A	3. A
4. D	4. D	4. C
5. B	5. B	5. A
6. A	6. A	6. B
7. A	7. D	7. D
8. B	8. C	8. C
9. B	9. B	9. A
10. A	10. B	10. B

Unit 1 Lesson 4	Unit 1 Lesson 5	Unit 1 Lesson 6
1. D	1. C	1. B
2. B	2. B	2. C
3. A	3. C	3. A
4. C	4. D	4. D
5. B	5. A	5. C
6. A	6. B	6. B
7. A	7. D	7. C
8. C	8. B	8. D
9. D	9. A	9. A
10. B	10. C	10. B

UNIT 2—IDENTIFYING DETAILS

Unit 2 Lesson 7	Unit 2 Lesson 8	Unit 2 Lesson 9
1. C	1. C	1. A
2. A	2. A	2. D
3. C	3. B	3. C
4. D	4. C	4. B
5. A	5. D	5. A
6. C	6. D	6. C
7. B	7. C	7. A
8. D	8. B	8. B
9. B	9. A	9. D
10. A	10. B	10. B

Unit 2 Lesson 10	Unit 2 Lesson 11	Unit 2 Lesson 12
1. C	1. B	1. B
2. B	2. D	2. C
3. D	3. C	3. A
4. A	4. A	4. D
5. B	5. B	5. A
6. A	6. A	6. D
7. A	7. C	7. C
8. B	8. A	8. D
9. C	9. B	9. B
10. D	10. D	10. D

UNIT 3—UNDERSTANDING THE MAIN IDEA

Unit 3 Lesson 13	Unit 3 Lesson 14	Unit 3 Lesson 15
1. B	1. B	1. C
2. A	2. D	2. B
3. B	3. B	3. B
4. A	4. C	4. A
5. D	5. A	5. B
6. C	6. B	6. D
7. C	7. C	7. B
8. D	8. A	8. C
9. B	9. D	9. D
10. D	10. C	10. A

Unit 3 Lesson 16	Unit 3 Lesson 17	Unit 3 Lesson 18
1. A	1. A	1. C
2. D	2. B	2. A
3. D	3. D	3. D
4. C	4. B	4. C
5. C	5. C	5. D
6. B	6. C	6. B
7. C	7. A	7. B
8. A	8. D	8. C
9. B	9. B	9. A
10. C	10. C	10. C

UNIT 4—USING THE CONTEXT

Unit 4 Lesson 19	Unit 4 Lesson 20	Unit 4 Lesson 21
1. A	1. D	1. B
2. D	2. A	2. A
3. C	3. C	3. D
4. A	4. B	4. C
5. B	5. A	5. B
6. A	6. B	6. C
7. C	7. C	7. A
8. D	8. D	8. C
9. B	9. A	9. D
10. C	10. B	10. B

Unit 4 Lesson 22	Unit 4 Lesson 23	Unit 4 Lesson 24
1. B	1. C	1. C
2. A	2. A	2. B
3. D	3. B	3. A
4. C	4. D	4. D
5. B	5. C	5. B
6. D	6. B	6. D
7. B	7. C	7. C
8. A	8. A	8. A
9. B	9. D	9. B
10. C	10. B	10. C

UNIT 5—DRAWING CONCLUSIONS

Unit 5 Lesson 25	Unit 5 Lesson 26	Unit 5 Lesson 27
1. B	1. B	1. B
2. D	2. C	2. C
3. A	3. B	3. A
4. D	4. C	4. D
5. B	5. D	5. B
6. C	6. A	6. D
7. B	7. A	7. A
8. D	8. B	8. B
9. C	9. D	9. C
10. A	10. C	10. A

Unit 5 Lesson 28	Unit 5 Lesson 29	Unit 5 Lesson 30
1. D	1. B	1. B
2. B	2. D	2. D
3. A	3. C	3. C
4. B	4. A	4. A
5. C	5. B	5. D
6. A	6. B	6. A
7. B	7. D	7. B
8. D	8. C	8. C
9. A	9. A	9. A
10. C	10. C	10. B

UNIT 6—MAKING INFERENCES

Unit 6 Lesson 31	Unit 6 Lesson 32	Unit 6 Lesson 33
1. B	1. B	1. D
2. C	2. A	2. B
3. B	3. C	3. A
4. A	4. A	4. C
5. D	5. D	5. A
6. A	6. A	6. C
7. D	7. B	7. A
8. C	8. D	8. B
9. C	9. B	9. A
10. B	10. C	10. D

Unit 6 Lesson 34	Unit 6 Lesson 35	Unit 6 Lesson 36
1. A	1. B	1. B
2. D	2. A	2. A
3. A	3. B	3. C
4. B	4. C	4. B
5. A	5. B	5. D
6. D	6. A	6. C
7. C	7. D	7. A
8. B	8. C	8. C
9. A	9. A	9. D
10. C	10. D	10. A